Progress in Construction Science and Technology No. 2

Edited by:

Roger A. Burgess, BArch, ARIBA, FIOB, FIWSP
Professor of Construction, University of Salford

Peter J. Horrobin, MA, ARIC
Visiting Lecturer, Department of Building, University of Manchester Institute of Science and Technology

John W. Simpson, BSc, MSc, MInstP
Senior Lecturer in Building, University of Manchester Institute of Science and Technology

MTP

MEDICAL AND TECHNICAL PUBLISHING CO LTD
1973

Published by
Medical and Technical Publishing Co Ltd
P.O. Box 55
St. Leonard's House
St. Leonardgate
Lancaster

SBN 852 00054 5

First Published 1973

A/690

PRINTED AND BOUND IN GREAT BRITAIN BY
HAZELL WATSON AND VINEY LTD
AYLESBURY, BUCKS

Progress in Construction Science
and Technology
No. 2

Preface

Our aim in producing the first volume of Progress in Construction Science and Technology was to provide a vehicle for the publication of comprehensive review articles on topics which have application to the many divisions of the construction industry. The success of that first volume, measured by the response it has provoked from readers and the comments made by reviewers gives us confidence that our aim was fulfilled. We therefore present this second issue, knowing that the formula by which it is compiled has already received the approval of the market we were aiming to reach.

We are grateful to our team of authors for the efforts they have made to write such useful contributions to this volume and hope that this will in turn stimulate the submission of further papers for inclusion in subsequent issues of Progress in Construction Science and Technology.

Once again, although we are no longer all members of the Department of Building of the University of Manchester Institute of Science and Technology, it is our pleasure to acknowledge all the help and co-operation that our colleagues and former colleagues in that Department have so willingly offered. We are grateful to them.

ROGER BURGESS
PETER HORROBIN
JOHN SIMPSON

Manchester, February 1973

Contents

1

The use of models in the design of buildings

Henry J. Cowan, DEng, PhD, MSc, FIEAust,
FRSA, FIStructE, FASCE
Professor of Architectural Science
University of Sydney, Australia.

1.1. THE SPECIAL PROBLEMS OF THE BUILDING INDUSTRY

Building differs from most other manufacturing industries. Its products are quite expensive, but generally only one article is made to each design. Disastrous failures are not likely, and design is therefore comparatively superficial. The cost of designing a building is between 5–10 per cent of the total; and the cost of designing the structure, which is the part most amenable to model analysis, is of the order of 1 per cent of the total cost of the building. So it is often preferable to use an approximate calculation than to employ a precise analysis.

This is not true of the design of most other commodities. The cost of designing a plastic case for a radio receiver is many times the cost of a single receiver. This is not important because a great many receivers are made to a single design.

To take another example, the number of aeroplanes produced to a single design may be small. But aeroplanes must be very light, and to achieve this, they are designed with a low factor of structural safety. The cost of design is a large part of the cost of the aeroplane; however, this is unavoidable if the plane is to operate economically.

The design of dams poses different problems again. A dam retaining the water in a reservoir is a compact form of structure, and an expensive one. Its shape is largely determined by the shape of the surrounding rock. Although it is a one-off structure, model analysis is extensively employed because it is a small item in the cost, because failure would be disastrous, and because the shape is so irregular that theoretical solutions are difficult.

None of these arguments apply to the design of buildings. One cannot afford to break a complete full-size architectural structure as one can break a prototype plastic radio casing. It need not be designed with as low a factor of safety as in aircraft design; although weight costs money, a concrete floor with excessive structural depth may help with sound insulation and fire protection, and ultimately prove economical. If the structure is misdesigned, it will usually show signs of distress in good time, while the aeroplane may disintegrate in mid-air. If the shape proves mathematically too complex, we can change it, whereas we cannot change the boundaries of a dam. The simplified geometry of the building may look a little different from the original concept, but a good deal of latitude is possible within the framework of modern mathematical techniques.

Many of the techniques used in the model analysis of architectural structures are derived from the general manufacturing industry, the aircraft industry, and from the design of dams; not all are economical when applied to buildings.

The problems are much the same in other aspects of building design. We can use models for the design of the acoustic, lighting and thermal environment, but these have remained research, rather than design tools, partly because most of the problems are amenable to calculation, even if approximate, and partly because there is a substantial tolerance of error. If a concert-hall falls down, something has to be done about it; if its acoustics are poor, we may put up with them for a century.

Not surprisingly, perhaps, it is in its least scientific aspects that the architectural model has so far been most successful. Most architects use a model to show the appearance of the building. These models are generally viewed from above, i.e. the point of view of an observer in an aeroplane, and consequently do not convey a correct impression. This defect could be readily corrected with a small periscope; but few people use one. The model is a means of explaining the architectural concept to the layman; it helps the architect to visualize the entire scheme; it is rarely used for detailed architectural design, which is done on paper.

Another field in which visual models are now used is in the installation of the services. A 1:48 scale model was made for the New South Wales State Office Block, a thirty-five storey government office building recently completed in Sydney. This can be separated at each floor, so that each installation can be examined in detail (1). A similar model has also been made for the services in the Sydney Opera House.

This 'public relations' aspect of model design has not been considered sufficiently in architectural science. Even where a structural model may not be the best means of obtaining the detailed dimensions of a structure, it can often help the architect and his client, and often also the structural consultant, to obtain a better appreciation of the problem. Much of the same applies to models of lighting, ventilation, acoustics, and sight-lines in theatres.

The inter-relation of the various forms of model analysis also has not received sufficient attention. Thus a complex roof-shape needs to be tested in a wind-tunnel to obtain the distribution of wind-pressure and suction, since there is virtually no theoretical solution to this problem if the shape departs much from simple geometry. A model of the roof shape, with holes for measuring wind-pressure, forms an excellent mould to make a plastic model for structural analysis, and the cost of the latter is reduced accordingly. It is often possible to use architectural or structural models for a lighting analysis, if this point is considered initially, and so on. Model analysis could therefore be more economical if the various aspects were considered together initially, with due allowance for the scale factors appropriate to various forms of analysis.

1.2. EXPERIMENT VERSUS THEORY

The main obstacle to the wider use of models in architectural science, however, is the rapid advance of theory.

Theoretical and experimental analysis are essentially complementary forms of structural design. Advances in theory tend to reduce reliance on experimental solutions, and vice versa.

Models were occasionally used in the Middle Ages and the Renaissance. Domenico Fontana describes in his published account of the erection of the obelisk outside St. Peter's in Rome, how he designed the layout of the hoisting ropes with a model lead obelisk (2), but there are no fully authenticated examples of model analysis for the structural design of buildings from that period.

In the late 18th century the elastic theory made rapid progress, and iron was used more and more for structural design in the next few decades. Empirical rules gave way to theoretical calculations, and structural systems were adapted to the existing simple theory. However, before the 20th century the theory of structures was never used successfully for the design of the more complex masonry and concrete vaults and domes, which continued to be designed by empirical rules.

The growing sophistication of structural theory was largely

responsible for the increasing complexity of engineered structures in the 20th century. This encouraged the search for a mechanized form of structural design as calculations became more laborious.

The apparatus devised by Professor G. E. Beggs at Princeton University in 1922, (3), the first successful method of model analysis, and other early examples may be regarded as mechanical analogues of the elastic theory, rather than scale models of a part of the building. Their significance lay in the fact that they gave the same answer as the mathematical solution; it was incidental that the model dimensions were proportional to those of the structure.

In other fields of engineering the theory of dimensional analysis was well established in the early 20th century. Scale models were regularly used for hydraulic works, and in the 1920's wind-tunnels were commonly employed to test scale models of aeroplanes and aeroplane parts.

The techniques of structural model analysis were greatly improved during the same period; but the significant development of the early 1930's was the discovery of the Moment-Distribution Method by Professor Hardy Cross, which made the design of linear rigid frames much simpler by calculation.

At the same time imaginative reinforced concrete structures of complex shape began to make their appearance in Southern Europe. Both Nervi and Torroja used small scale models in their design (4, 5). During the Second World War aircraft design made great progress, and structural design of aeroplanes with the aid of scale models instrumented with the new miniature electric resistance strain gauges was carried to a high degree of perfection. In the late 1940's the method was applied to architectural structures, and rapid design solutions were obtained for problems hitherto soluble only by exceedingly lengthy calculations.

The Second World War had produced another powerful design tool which took a little longer to be adapted to structural design. In the 1950's digital computer solutions for structural problems became available, and the scope of computer-based design is steadily increasing. If the picture had altered rapidly in favour of model design, it now shifted again the other way.

The rapid change has been caused by remarkable progress in structural analysis. Opinions may differ on the aesthetic merits of the 'Architecture of Structural Excitement'; but there is little doubt about the technical advances. The patterns of Beggs' Apparatus available in 1968 are superior to the original 1922 version; but we have better techniques of theoretical design, and this form of model analysis is now obsolete.

Is structural model analysis then merely an historical interlude, or has it a definite place in architectural design? For a proper assessment one must take account of two other aspects. One is the realism of model design. The true scale model, unlike the digital computer, is more than a structural analogue. It can copy the exact degree of rigidity, the continuity of adjacent structural members, and the irregular openings which architectural planning may demand. These can be incorporated only with difficulty in a mathematical solution, if at all.

The second factor is the new importance of the non-specialist, and the growing use of model techniques for other aspects of architectural design (visual models, environmental models, etc.). The client's point of view is not merely important because he pays the bill. He often has an unrivalled knowledge of the requirements of the building, and he can thus help the architect and the specialist consultants, if he understands their problems. The architect, in turn, cannot be expected to know the details of structural theory, and the various consultants may be equally unfamiliar with one another's specialties. At the present time, computer programmes are no help to understanding the problems of other experts. Models, however, are frequently obvious enough to be readily intelligible. If the concept of the integrated design of buildings is to become accepted, communication of ideas will need to be greatly improved. The value of model analysis cannot be measured merely by comparing the cost of a theoretical solution for a given set of boundary conditions with that of a model solution for the same boundary conditions. One must also enquire whether the boundary conditions can be expressed in mathematical terms, and whether the result can be explained to all members of the design team who should understand the implications.

1.3. DIMENSIONAL THEORY

Scaling is introduced as soon as one abandons the full-scale testing practised in the 17th and 18th century. Galileo noticed that a fly blown up to the size of an elephant would not be able to stand up, and scaling is not necessarily proportional (6).

Dimensional similarity presents few problems, so long as one does not deal with dynamic problems, such as earthquakes and explosions, with temperature stresses, or with ultimate strength. For static loading within the elastic range it is only necessary to produce an exactly scaled model, and keep the ratio W/EL^2 constant (1). The model and the structural material should also have the same Poisson's ratio, but departure from this dimensional rule causes only a small error.

It is best to use a model material with a low modulus of elasticity and a high elastic limit, to get the highest possible strains, so that even the parts of the model with small strains present measurable results. Several plastics, such as Perspex, are in that category, but most suffer from creep, which imposes a careful timetabling on the measurements. The model load is reduced with the square of the scale, so that a small model can easily be loaded with dead weights or with an airbag. If the material has a high elastic limit, one can overload the model to get higher strain readings, so long as one allows for it in the load factor. A trial run will establish that.

The scale is often determined by the commercially available sheet or bar for the most common model dimensions. For example, Sydney University was able to make a cheap model analysis for a *skew* concrete bridge, because it was a flat slab of uniform thickness with two central circular columns, and it was possible to find a scale ratio which made the slab and the column stock Perspex sizes. If it had been necessary to machine the Perspex the model might have priced itself out by comparison with a computer analysis.

A constant scale factor for all dimensions is not always possible. It may be difficult to get the right materials, and rolled steel sections can, of course, only be modelled by equivalent rectangles. Another problem arises if a shell is originally designed to be, say, $3\frac{1}{2}$ in (88 mm) thick, and the preliminary model analysis shows that this can be reduced to 3 in (75 mm). If a new model is not warranted by the size of the structure, we now have two scale factors, one for thickness and one for span. The load interpretation can only be right for stress *or* for deflections, not both. One has to choose which is more important.

1.4. INSTRUMENTATION

Model analysis became possible only when strain measuring instruments were devised which were both light and had short gauge-lengths. The first of these was the Huggenberger Tensometer, a Swiss compound-lever mechanical gauge, developed about 1930. A dozen Huggenberger Tensometers will amply repay the initial capital cost, if a lot of model testing is to be done, because they can be re-used indefinitely. There is also a demountable version, i.e. one instrument suffices for as many gauge points as desired; but it is, of course, not as accurate.

For precision work and remote reading, electric resistance strain gauges are best, and with rosettes a complete picture of strain distribution is obtainable. The price of an electric resistance gauge, including attachment to the model and connection to the electric circuit is approximately $1·50 in Australia. However, quite a lot of capital equipment is required, if large numbers of gauges are to be used. We now use a temperature compensated switching unit and a digital voltmeter, which makes it possible to record the results directly on punched tape. This produces a systematic and accurate record, which can be evaluated and typed by computer without any intermediate manual recording. This is particularly helpful if strain rosettes are used.

At one time a large number of strain measurements could create an *embarassment des richesses*, and it was simply not feasible to reduce all the results to stress data. The computer does that at a greatly reduced cost. But it is still true that the number of strain gauges should be kept to a minimum. They add to the cost, and there is always a danger that wires are mis-connected, with disastrous results. An error of this sort is difficult to trace on a complex model.

Deflection, which is often much harder to obtain theoretically than strain, is very easily measured on a model. An ordinary dial gauge has ample sensitivity, even where deflections are small.

1.5. MODEL MATERIALS

For analysis within the elastic range, the choice lies mainly between metals, thermoplastics and casting resins. Plaster and cement mortar

Fig. 1.1. Model of a suspension structure, tested by Mr. D. Epstein at Sydney University.

are especially useful for ultimate strength, but their strain capacity is too small for mainly elastic testing.

Metal is particularly useful for suspension structures. Fig. 1.1 shows the model of a suspension roof with structural roof sheeting, before the strain guages and loads were attached.

Thermosplastic sheet or bar, such as Perspex, is easy to form in a constant-temperature oven, it is easy to cut, drill and turn, and it is easy to weld. A whole range of sizes is available commercially, but creep is a problem.

Casting resins, with or without glass fibre reinforcement, can be produced in any form or thickness, but dimensional accuracy of thin sections is hard to achieve. There is little trouble with creep, but shrinkage stresses during setting can cause serious cracking, and damage the elastic strain capacity.

Table 1.1. *Properties of plastics*

Property	Acrylic resins (Perspex, Lucite, Plexiglas)	Cellulose nitrate (Celluloid)	Phenolics (Bakelite)	Polyester resin	Epoxy resin	Polyvinyl-chloride
Classification	thermoplastic	thermoplastic	thermosetting	thermosetting	thermosetting	thermoplastic
Modulus of elasticity lbf/in² (MN/m²)	$4 \cdot 5 \times 10^5$ (3100)	$0 \cdot 65{-}40 \times 10^5$ (420–27 600)	$5 \cdot 5{-}7 \cdot 5 \times 10^5$ (3790–5160)	$3 \cdot 0{-}5 \cdot 5 \times 10^5$ (2090–3790)	$2 \cdot 0{-}6 \cdot 0 \times 10^5$ (1380–4140)	$4 \cdot 0{-}5 \cdot 0 \times 10^5$ (2760–3450)
Poisson's ratio	0·36	0·41	0·36	0·40	0·40	0·40
Tensile strength lbf/in² (MN/m²)	8000–10 000 (55·2–68·9)	3000–7000 (20·7–48·2)	7000–15 000 (48·2–103)	3500–10 000 (24·1–68·9)	5000–12 000 (34·5–82·7)	5000–10 000 (34·5–68·9)
Compressive strength lbf/in² (MN/m²)	12 000–20 000 (82·7–138)	3000–30 000 (20·7–207)	10 000–25 000 (68·9–172)	12 000–20 000 (82·7–138)	15 000–30 000 (103–207)	10 000–12 000 (68·9–82·7)
Elongation at rupture per cent	3–10	40–90	1	5	5–10	2–40
Softening point °C	80–98	70	—	—	—	82
Coeff. of linear expansion cm °C/cm	$5{-}9 \times 10^{-5}$	$11{-}17 \times 10^{-5}$	4×10^{-5}	6×10^{-5}	$5{-}9 \times 10^{-5}$	5×10^{-5}
Machinability	Excellent	Excellent	Good	Fair	Good	Excellent

1.6. THE VALUE OF SMALL PLASTIC MODELS

Sydney University's Architectural Science Department has developed a strong preference for small Perspex models, because the cost of making models is generally much higher than the cost of testing. It is a relatively simple matter to make a small, but geometrically accurate, model in Perspex, and dimensional accuracy is a prime requirement in model analysis. With size, cost increases sharply, because the price of constant temperature ovens, used in forming Perspex, increases sharply with size, loading becomes more expensive, and creep problems increase, with consequent multiplication of strain readings.

Small models have evident limitations. It is not possible to get many strain gauges on them, or use other than short gauge-lengths. They are, however, quite adequate for small structures, and for a preliminary assessment of large structures.

The majority of complex structures have modest spans, say up to 150 ft (45 m), and that it is within that range that architects are most inclined to use unorthodox forms.

Fig. 1.2*a* shows the structural model for a design for a memorial chapel in Sydney. Various sections of the roof, taken off the architect's drawings, were cut out in cardboard, and used as templates for a plaster mould. The Perspex model was then formed in a constant-temperature oven, by putting a flat sheet on the mould, and gradually pressing it down with sandbags. Another, stiffer, model was made for the wind-tunnel test (Fig. 1.2*b*). A demountable strain gauge was then used to locate the highest stresses, and the electric resistance strain gauges were placed thereon. Deflection is, of course, important for the design of this sort of structure, and this is easily and accurately obtained by a model, whereas even if the theory is known, it is troublesome to compute theoretically. A test on a small model like this costs only a few hundred pounds. Since high precision is not required, a few strain gauges are sufficient.

Even for large structures a small preliminary model is worthwhile. An elaborate plastic model with hundreds of strain gauges was used in the design of the Sydney Opera House, but by that time the foundations were already constructed. If a small preliminary model had

Fig. 1.2. (*a*) Wind Tunnel model of a saddle roof for a church in Sydney, tested by Mr. G. D. Ding at Sydney University and (*b*) Structural model.

been built right at the beginning, it might have saved some of the trouble which subsequently occurred.

1.7. LIMITATIONS OF OTHER METHODS

It has been argued that plastic models are of limited value because they cannot be taken beyond the elastic range; but this overlooks the

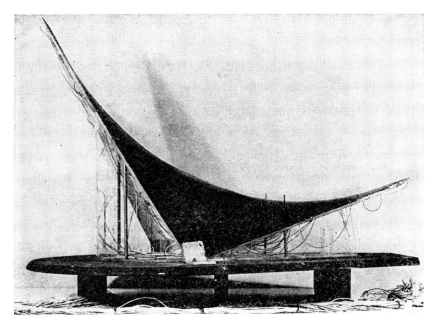

Fig. 1.2. (*b*).

fact that it is extremely rare to make calculations both for the elastic range and for ultimate strength. A shell structure is normally designed by the elastic theory, and the model is simply as an analogue computer for doing the same thing. If the building is large and expensive, then the cost of a reinforced mortar model for ultimate strength tests is, of course, warranted once it has been decided to proceed with the design (7).

While reinforced mortar models may be unduly elaborate, particularly for preliminary tests and for the smaller spans, some of the cheaper techniques used in the experimental stress analysis of machine parts have not been useful in architecture.

For example, the cost of making and testing models by photo-elasticity and the brittle-lacquer technique is relatively modest in a laboratory which has the necessary equipment and know-how. Unfortunately the stress-gradients in architectural structures are rarely sufficient for accurate results.

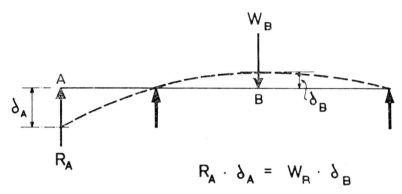

Fig. 1.3. Müller-Breslau's theorem.

The Moiré method should be mentioned, since not everybody is familiar with it. The variation devised by Professor Durelli, now at the Catholic University in Washington, is particularly simple (8). It is only necessary to obtain sheets of the transparent grids of parallel lines used by printers for making half-tone blocks, and paste them at right angles, one on the model and one on a fixed reference sheet. Although there is a superficial similarity to the isochromatic lines of photo-elasticity, one measures the radius of curvature (i.e. slope) and the other differences between the two principal stresses. The patterns of the Moiré method, using ordinary printer's screens, are more sensitive than photo-elastic patterns on the same Plexiglas model, but so far no application has been found in architectural structures which would be solved more easily by this means than either by calculation or strain gauges.

The various indirect methods suffer from the same limitation, although they have an undoubted value in teaching structural behaviour. Most of these methods are based on Müller-Breslau's theorem (Fig. 1.3) which gives the relation between the forces at two points A and B and the resulting deflections. If we apply a unit deformation at A and measure the resulting deformation at some point along the beam, B, this is numerically equal to the statically indeterminate reaction at A caused by a unit load at B. This means that the shape of the deflected member is the influence line for the reaction.

Beggs' Deformeter has already been mentioned. It has since been shown that the small displacements, which Beggs took so much

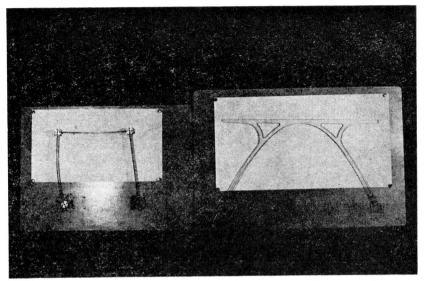

Fig. 1.4. Indirect models for (*a*) a portal and (*b*) an arch with two cantilever overhangs, which form the off-the-ground support for a block of flats.

trouble to obtain, are generally unnecessary. The large-deflection models (Fig. 1.4) obviate the need for the eye-strain caused by the micrometer microscope, since it is only necessary to count the squares on a piece of graph paper.

However, the model in Fig. 1.4*a*, which gives quite an accurate result, does not improve on the moment distribution method. The structure represented by Fig. 1.4*b* would have to be solved by strain energy, which could be quite time-consuming if the curve did not conform to a simple mathematical equation. But the indirect method is here liable to be seriously in error, since the model only determines the moment due to the statically indeterminate reactions, M_r (Fig. 1.5). The net bending moment

$$M = M_w - M_r$$

where M_w is the statically determinate bending moment due to the loads. This is, of course, the reason why arches are so efficient for long spans. However, in indirect model analysis one faces the problem that an unavoidable small error may be greatly enlarged in the subtraction. This never happens in direct model analysis with strain gauges.

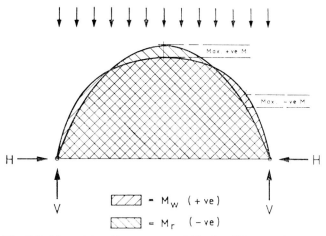

Fig. 1.5. The net bending moment M is the difference between the statically determinate bending moment M_w and the statically indeterminate bending moment M_r obtained from the indirect model.

There are numerous improved versions of the method based on the Müller-Breslau theorem. Professor Charlton (9) has described them most ably; but none can do anything that a digital computer could not do quicker and more accurately.

The practical use of model analysis therefore lies mainly in the range where a computer either cannot be used to get a solution because there is as yet no programme, or as a simple approximate preliminary analysis which shows up the behaviour of the structure, and perhaps serves to convince the architect and the client that it would be better to think again before a lot of money is spent on a more detailed investigation. The range of useful model solutions is perhaps narrowing. Twelve years ago Sydney University was able to solve a rather complex steel frame by model analysis in six weeks, whereas no answer had been obtained by computer at the end of three months (10). Today a computer would certainly do this quicker and cheaper.

1.8. SOME CASE HISTORIES

In conclusion, a few additional examples are given of work done in Australia.

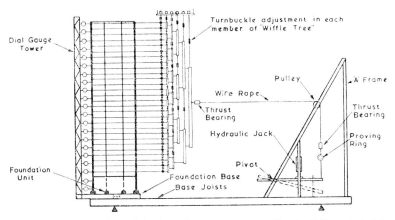

Fig. 1.6. Loading of model of reinforced concrete office building, tested by Professor F. S. Shaw and Mr. P. Balint at the University of New South Wales.

1.8.1. Australia Square Tower

The Australia Square Tower was completed in Sydney in 1967 (11). This is a circular concrete frame, 600 ft (183 m) high. The floors are carried on a concrete service core and an outer ring of columns. The structure is about 12 000-fold statically indeterminate. The University of New South Wales made a model from polyester casting resin, 20 ft (6·1 m) high, with a scale ratio of 30:1. Each floor was cast separately, and polymerised at 150°F (65·6°C) for three hours. 500 electric resistance strain gauges were used. Wind loading was applied by a single lever system (Fig. 1.6).

1.8.2. Academy of Sciences in Canberra

This is a small dome with large cutouts standing in a pool of water (12) It was built in 1956 when little was known in Australia about concrete domes. It is only 146 ft (44·5 m) in diameter, but the sixteen arched openings present a problem. The University of Melbourne made a 4 ft (1·22 m) diameter model, to a scale of 40:1, from epoxy-resin impregnated glass fibre cloth.

1.8.3. Granville Club

This is a club for the Returned Services League (10). It is a folded plate dome with cut outs and irregularly spaced columns, but it is

Fig. 1.7. Perspex model of folded-plate dome for club in Sydney, tested by Professor H. J. Cowan at Sydney University.

only 82 ft (25 m) diameter. The consulting engineer assumed initially concrete thicknesses ranging from 12 in. (305 mm) to 4 in. (102 mm). A Perspex dome 30 in. (762 mm) diameter was made to a scale ratio of 32:1 (Fig. 1.7); it soon became clear that some of the assumed thicknesses were too high, and the results were interpreted by taking differential scale ratios for different parts of the structure.

/3 503/3/

The Australian concrete code permits three kinds of analysis; (i) by the elastic theory, (ii) by ultimate strength, and (iii) by model analysis. In the last case calculations were not required, if the test is done by an approved laboratory; however, the Granville Club is the only building ever designed under that clause. Some field measurements were taken when the formwork was removed, and correlation with the model test was quite good.

1.8.4. Centre-Point Tower

This is a twelve-storey building now under construction, situated between the two largest department stores, and providing communication between them at various levels. It is to be surmounted by a 650 ft (198 m) guyed tower which carries a two-storey revolving restaurant. The model was made of steel to a scale of 1:1000. Attaching strain gauges satisfactorily to the 0·064 in. (1·63 mm) diameter wire presented some problems.

1.8.5. Horseshoe-bearing for optical telescope

The Anglo-Australian 150-inch optical telescope now under construction near Coonabarabran in New South Wales, is to be mounted on a horse-shoe bearing carried on Coudé struts. Perspex models to a scale of 1:12·7 were used to determine the elastic deformation of the steel structure under its own weight as it rotated (Fig. 1·8). Stresses in the structure are very low, and not critical; however, misalignment has to be kept to a very low level for the satisfactory functioning of the instrument, and several alternative designs were examined.

1.8.6. Construction model for the Sydney Opera House

An elaborate model was made of the erection truss, to check the procedure proposed for the assembly of the precast segments for the Sydney Opera House. This was made on brass to a scale of 1:24, complete with an electric motor caused the truss to elongate the arc length whilst maintaining a constant radius, as was required in the prototype. All connections were made through spherical joints onto miniature railway tracks to facilitate longitudinal movement after each rib had been fully erected.

A/690

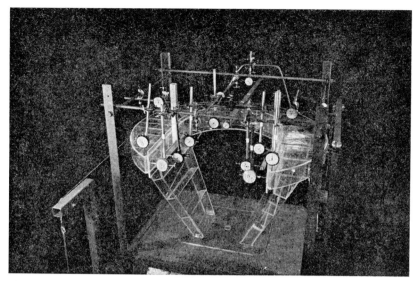

Fig. 1.8. Perspex model of a design for the steel structure supporting a 150-inch optical telescope, tested by Professor H. J. Cowan at Sydney University.

1.9. CONCLUSION

Models thus have a definite place in the scientific design of buildings, although perhaps not quite the central one which is sometimes proposed. High accuracy can only be achieved at great expense, but there is ample scope for investigating qualitative problems, as in the construction model of the Opera House, or make preliminary design investigations, as in the proposal shown in Fig. 1·2 which is a complex solution for a small-span structure. There will occasionally be problems which can be solved with high accuracy more easily than with a computer. The skew bridge, which happened to fit Perspex stock sizes is one example, and many deflection problems are in that category; but these will decline in significance as computer solutions become simpler.

This will still leave a good range of problems, particularly where discussion between the engineer, the architect and the client is necessary.

REFERENCES

1. COWAN, H. J., GERO, J. S., DING, G. D. and MUNCEY, R. W. (1968). *Models in Architecture* (London: Elsevier).
2. COWAN, H. J. (1966). An Historical Outline of Architectural Science, p. 16 (Amsterdam: Elsevier).
3. BEGGS, G. E. (1922). 'The accurate mechanical solution of statically indeterminate structures by the use of paper models and special gauges.' *J. Am. Conc. Inst.* **18**, 58–78.
4. NERVI, P. L. (1955). 'La ricerche statici sperimentali su modelli.' (Research on experimental stress analysis with models). *Costruire Corretamente*, chap. 6, p. 105–113 (Milan: Hoepli).
5. *The Structures of Eduardo Torroja*, p. 97–99. (1958). (New York: F. W. Dodge).
6. GALILEO GALILEI *Two New Sciences*. Transl. by H. Vrew and A. d. Alavio (1933). p. 115 (New York: Macmillan).
7. JONES, L. L. and BASE, G. D. (1965). 'Test of a twelfth-scale model of the dome of the shell roof for Smithfield Poultry Market.' *Proc. Inst. Civ. Eng.* **30**, 109–130.
8. DURELLI, A. J. and PARKS, V. J. (1970). *Moire Analysis of Strain* (Englewood Cliffs: Prentice-Hall).
9. CHARLTON, T. M. (1966). *Model Analysis of Plane Structures* (Oxford: Pergamon).
10. COWAN, H. J. (1961). 'Some applications of the use of direct model analysis in the design of architectural structures.' *J. Inst. Engs. Aust.* **33**, 259–267.
11. BALINT, P. S. and SHAW, F. S. (1965). 'Structural model of the Australia Square Tower in Sydney.' *Arch. Sci. Rev.* (Sydney) **8**, 136–149.
12. STEVENS, L. K. (1959). 'Investigations on a model dome with arched cut-outs.' *Mag. Conc. Res.* **11**, 3–14.

2

Developments in structural masonry

Professor A. W. Hendry, DSc., FIStructE., FRSE
Department of Civil Engineering and Building Science
The University of Edinburgh

2.1. Introduction

2.2. Wall layout and stability
    2.2.1. Factors influencing wall layout
    2.2.2. Typical wall arrangements

2.3. The strength of brickwork and blockwork
    2.3.1. Masonry testing and the code of practice
    2.3.2. Compressive strength of masonry
    2.3.3. Strength of masonry in combined compression and shear
    2.3.4. The strength of masonry in flexure

2.4. Wind load analysis of multi-storey masonry structures

2.5. Design for accidental damage
    2.5.1. The emergence of the problem
    2.5.2. The resistance of brickwork to gas explosions
    2.5.3. Limitation of accidental damage

2.6. Conclusion

2.1. INTRODUCTION

There is no doubt that the past decade has seen a major advance in the design of brickwork and blockwork building structures not only in the United Kingdom but in Europe, North America and Australia. This advance has been comprehensively documented in the proceedings of two international conferences (1, 2) which together provide a wealth of information for designers. The purpose of the present article is to review certain aspects of structural design in brickwork and blockwork in the light of recent research work. The article will be concerned mainly with practice and research in the United Kingdom and will deal principally with unreinforced clay brickwork, which at present is the most important form of structural masonry in this country.

2.2. WALL LAYOUT AND STABILITY

2.2.1. Factors influencing wall layout

The first engineering problem in the design of a masonry building is to ensure the satisfactory deployment of the load bearing walls. In reaching a solution to this problem close collaboration is necessary between architect and structural engineer because of the multi-purpose nature of masonry walls, including subdivision of space, thermal and acoustic insulation, fire and weather protection as well as resistance to vertical and horizontal loads. In normal load bearing construction it is necessary to make the walls continuous from foundation to roof level. This means that the form of construction is best suited to those buildings in which the floor plan is repeated on each storey, although efforts are being made (3, 4, 5) to overcome this limitation by developing large span, some composite beams in which the floor slabs act as flanges and the walls as webs. In some existing buildings the provision of larger spaces in the lowermost floors of a multi-storey residential building has been achieved more conventionally by building these storeys in reinforced concrete and then changing over to load bearing masonry at the higher levels (6).

Leaving aside this complication, the main factors influencing the disposition of load-bearing walls are:

(*a*) The requirements of space sub-division

(*b*) The provision of lateral strength and rigidity

(*c*) Resistance to general failure following local accidental damage to the structure.

The last mentioned requirement has received wide attention in this country following the report (7) on a major structural failure of a multi-storey block of flats of precast concrete panel construction. This has subsequently led to specific provisions in the Building Regulations which may have an important influence on the disposition of load bearing walls. This problem will be discussed in detail in Section 2.5 of this article but from the point of view of the planning of a building, the main implication of the Fifth Amendment to the English Building Regulations lies (8) in the need to provide an arrangement of walls such that, in the event of a particular wall being damaged, the loads normally carried by it will be transmitted, with a reduced safety factor, to the foundations by adjacent walls acting in conjunction with the floor slabs. Situations requiring special consideration are likely to be found at the corners or gable walls of a building or in the vicinity of isolated strips of load bearing wall. In general terms, therefore, it will be desirable to provide return walls and spine walls and to look with some care at the effect of strip walls, particularly if they are at the corner of a building.

The provision of strength and rigidity against lateral forces, particularly wind effects, calls for the disposition of walls parallel to both the principal axes of the building. Alternatively, lateral strength may be provided by stair wells or service cores.

2.2.2. Typical wall arrangements

In practice, these basic structural requirements can usually be reconciled with architectural planning without undue difficulty and a wide variety of plan and elevational solutions has been produced. The simplest form of structure applicable to *slab* buildings, is the cross-wall form in which the main structure is provided by a series of parallel walls at right angles to the main axis of the building (Fig. 2.1). In such a building it is necessary to provide longitudinal walls for stability in this direction and in order to reduce liability to collapse of

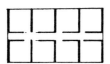

Fig. 2.1. Cross-wall structure.

Fig. 2.2. Cross-wall layout in a point block.

Fig. 2.3. Complex arrangement.

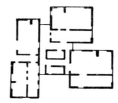

Fig. 2.4. Cellular arrangement.

a significant part of the building in the event of accidental damage to a main wall. With this type of structure there is complete freedom with regard to elevational treatment. An essentially similar wall arrangement is possible in point blocks, as exemplified in Fig. 2.2. In deeper buildings of the slab type there is likely to be a service core (Fig. 2.3) which may provide the entire lateral strength (9).

The second distinct type of wall arrangement is the cellular form in which both internal and external walls are load-bearing, with two way spanning slabs. Fig. 2.4 shows a typical example of this arrangement. This form requires, of course, that the elevations are in masonry but there is still ample scope for variations in the fenestration, and in the texture and colouring of the finishes.

Within these basic arrangements, examination of existing designs (10) shows that there is an unlimited variety of solutions available to meet particular circumstances and in this lies one of the most valuable features of brickwork construction.

2.3. THE STRENGTH OF BRICKWORK AND BLOCKWORK

2.3.1. Masonry testing and the code of practice

Early research work on load bearing brickwork sought to establish the strength of brickwork under various stress conditions in relation to conventional materials tests on the bricks and mortar. More recently, similar work has been carried out for blockwork as it was realised that, for a given strength, the dimensions of the unit have a considerable influence on the strength of the resulting masonry. Having established the strength of brickwork and blockwork on an empirical basis, basic permissible stresses were derived by the introduction of an arbitrary safety factor. This remains the basis of the current Code of Practice, CP 111 (1970), and although it results in safe structures it does not lead to a full understanding of the factors influencing the strength of masonry or of the mechanism of failure under stress. Such an understanding may or may not have a direct influence on the Code of Practice but when available will certainly help to rationalise the testing of masonry materials and will provide guidance in assessing possibilities of new or improved materials and in the interpretation of tests on masonry elements. Apart from this, there is the purely intellectual desire for a scientific explanation of observed phenomena. A discussion of the recent more rational approach to masonry strength may therefore be of some value. Almost all the work so far carried out on this topic has been related to brickwork but similar principles will apply also to blockwork.

2.3.2. Compressive strength of masonry

Indications from standard tests. A number of important points have been derived from compression tests on brickwork and associated standard materials tests. These include, firstly, the observation that brickwork loaded in uniform compression usually fails by the development of tension cracks parallel to the axis of loading, that is as a result of tensile stresses at right angles to the primary compression. This fact has been well known since the early years of brickwork testing. Secondly, it is evident that the strength of brickwork in compression is much smaller than the nominal compressive strength of the bricks from which it is built, as given by a standard compression test. On the other hand, brickwork strength may greatly exceed the cube crushing strength of the mortar used in it. Finally, it has been shown that the compressive strength of brickwork varies, roughly, as the square root of the nominal brick crushing strength and as the third or fourth root of the mortar cube strength.

From these observations it has been inferred (a) that the secondary tensile stresses which cause splitting failure of the brickwork result from restrained deformation of the mortar in the bed joints of the brickwork; (b) that the apparent compressive strength of bricks in a standard crushing test is not a direct measure of the strength of the unit in brickwork, since the mode of failure is different in the two situations; (c) that mortar is able to withstand higher compressive stresses in a brickwork bed joint than in a cube test because of the bi-axial or tri-axial nature of the stressing in this situation.

Experiments on the interaction of brick and bed material. It is possible to detect a paradox in the evidence from normal brick-work testing summarised above, namely, that whilst the cube crushing strength of mortar is only weakly related to brickwork strength, by a third or fourth root relationship, yet the mortar exerts a controlling influence on the brickwork strength achieved. This has been demonstrated in experiments reported by Francis, Horman and Jerrems (11) in which it is shown that brickwork prisms consisting of loose bricks, the bedding planes of which were ground flat, achieved compressive strengths approximately twice as high as those obtained from prisms with normal mortar joints.

Table 2.1. *Effect of different joint materials on the compressive strength of 3-brick prisms. Brick faces ground flat: 6 specimens of each type tested. (Morsy, 1968).*

Joint material	Compressive strength
Steel	8198 ± 890 lbf/in^2
Plywood	6733 ± 687 ,, ,,
Hardboard	6370 ± 605 ,, ,,
Polythene	2467 ± 224 ,, ,,
Rubber with fibres	1699 ± 119 ,, ,,
Soft rubber	1014 ± 84 ,, ,,
No joint material	5410 ± 745 ,, ,,

The effect of bed material on brick prism strength was investigated in some detail by Morsy (12). In these experiments the bed material in a series of model brick piers was varied from rubber at one end of the scale to steel at the other. The results, summarised in Table 2.1, show that there is an eight fold change in the prism strength with the substitution of steel for rubber in the bed joints. In the case of rubber jointing material, the bricks failed in tension as a result of tensile stress induced by the deformation of the rubber. Steel in the bed joints, on the other hand, had the effect of restraining lateral deformation of the bricks and this induced a state of bi-axial compressive stress in them. Failure in this case was by crushing, as in a typical compression test. Mortar has properties intermediate between these extremes and such as to cause splitting rather than crushing failure of the bricks.

Formulae for brickwork strength based on elastic analysis. Consideration of the qualitative evidence such as discussed in the preceding paragraph has prompted a number of investigators to derive formulae for brickwork strength in compression based on an elastic analysis of the brick-mortar complex. The earliest attempt would appear to be that due to Haller (13), published in 1959. Haller's formula, however, results in values of brickwork strength greater than the uniaxial strength of brick and is thus not valid in a quantitative

Table 2.2. *Formulae for compressive strength of brickwork*

Francis
$$\sigma = \sigma_B \left[\frac{1 + \dfrac{E_m}{E_B}.\dfrac{d_m}{d_B}.\dfrac{(1 - \nu_B)}{(1 - \nu_m)}}{1 + \dfrac{\nu_m}{\nu}.\dfrac{d_m}{d_B}.\dfrac{\left(1 - \dfrac{\nu_B^2}{\nu_m}.\dfrac{E_m}{E_B}\right)}{(1 - \nu_m)}} \right]$$

Lenczner
$$\sigma = \sigma_B \left[\frac{1 + \dfrac{E_m}{E_B}.\dfrac{d_m}{d_B}.\dfrac{(1 - \nu_B)}{(1 - \nu_m)}}{1 + \dfrac{\nu_m}{\nu_B}.\dfrac{d_m}{d_B}.\dfrac{(1 - \nu_B)}{(1 - \nu_m)}} \right]$$

Hilsdorf
$$\sigma = \frac{\sigma_B}{U} \left[\frac{1 + \dfrac{1}{4\cdot1}.\dfrac{d_m}{d_B}.\dfrac{\sigma_m}{t_B}}{1 + \dfrac{1}{4\cdot1}.\dfrac{d_m}{d_B}.\dfrac{\sigma_B}{t_B}} \right]$$

σ—Brickwork compressive strength
σ_B—Uniaxial strength of brick
σ_m—Uniaxial strength of mortar
d_B—Thickness of brick
d_m—Thickness of mortar
E_B—Youngs modulus of brick

E_m—Youngs modulus of mortar
ν_B—Poisson's ratio for brick
ν_m—Poisson's ratio for mortar
t_B—Biaxial tensile strength of brick material
U—Non-uniformity coefficient.

sense. Very similar formulae have been derived by Lenczner (14) and by Francis (11); these are shown in Table 2.2 and are based on consideration of statical equilibrium and strain compatability at the mortar/brick interface.

The great difficulty in this approach to brickwork strength lies in the fact that the materials, particularly the mortar, are not elastic up to the point of failure and therefore the values of Young's modulus and Poisson's ratio for the two components of the system cannot be uniquely defined. It is possible that a non-linear analysis might be produced but it would be rather difficult to determine the necessary deformation characteristics experimentally. Notwithstanding this limitation, fair agreement has been demonstrated (11) with experimental results and the formulae do give some indication of the controlling factors involved.

Failure criterion based on consideration of multi-axial strength of bricks and mortar. An alternative approach to the definition of brickwork strength has been proposed by Hilsdorf (15), based on consid-

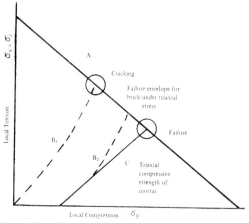

Fig. 2.5. Hilsdorf's failure criterion.

eration of the multi-axial strength of the component materials. Hilsdorf bases his analysis on an assumed linear relationship between lateral biaxial tensile strength and local compressive stress, equal to the mean external compressive stress multiplied by a 'non-uniformity' factor, U, as indicated in figure 2.5. When external compression is applied to the brickwork, internal tensile stresses are induced, following some line such as B, in Fig. 2.5. When this line intersects the failure criterion envelope, A, a local crack is developed in the brickwork. Further local cracks will appear on subsequent increase of load, but general failure will not take place until the brick can no longer provide the bi-axial restraint necessary to prevent failure of the mortar, or conversely, when the tri-axial state of stress developed in the brick exceeds its resistance to the existing combination of stresses. This will occur when the line defining the tri-axial strength of the mortar (C, in Fig. 2.5) intersects the failure line for the brickwork. Hilsdorf presented the result of his analysis as a formula which is given in Table 2.2 in a form modified to make it comparable with the elastic analysis formulae.

Hilsdorf demonstrated that this formula could be used to predict the strength of brickwork to within ± 20 per cent even although he was obliged to make a number of assumptions regarding the tri-axial strength of mortar and the bi-axial tensile strength of brick.

It would seem more feasible to carry out strength tests of the type necessary for Hilsdorf's approach than to attempt to measure deformation characteristics as would be required for the alternative method described above. Further work has therefore been carried out by Khoo on the lines proposed by Hilsdorf. This has resulted in the definition of the bi-axial tension/compression failure envelope for brick material and of the tri-axial compression strength of mortar (16, 17). The reduction of brick strength by the presence of an orthogonal tension was found to be more pronounced than had been postulated by Hilsdorf. The increase in compressive strength of mortar in the presence of a confining compression is quite considerable but less than has been found for concrete. Using this data a failure theory for the strength of axially loaded brickwork was obtained, which shows good correlation with experimental results obtained from crushing tests on brickwork prisms (Fig. 2.6).

The compressive strength of blockwork. Although far more detailed work has been carried out on the strength of brickwork than of blockwork, a number of points regarding the latter material can be deduced from the study of brickwork. For example, it has been shown that the

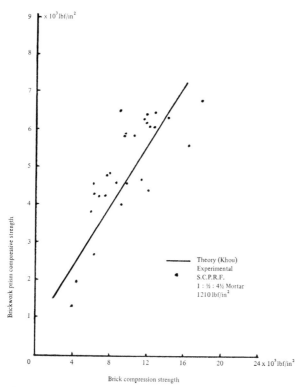

Fig. 2.6. Strength of brickwork prisms by failure theory of Khoo. Experimental points from S.C.P.R.F. National Testing Program.

ratio of brick height to joint thickness has an appreciable effect on brickwork strength—the thinner the joint the higher the masonry strength. As the relative joint thickness is much smaller in blockwork, one would expect that its strength in relation to the strength of the blocks used in its construction would be higher. On the other hand, as the ratio of height to thickness of a block is usually greater than in the case of a brick, the relationship of the nominal crushing strength of a block to the uni-axial compressive strength of the material will be different and therefore empirical strength values for brickwork will not be properly applicable to blockwork. This has been recognised and an addendum to CP 111 (1964) has been issued giving modification factors for shape of unit. Thus, blockwork built of blocks of nominal face size 18 in × 9 in and 3 in or 4 in thickness is permitted double the basic permissible stress in compression set out for brickwork. Using blocks of 6 in and $8\frac{3}{4}$ in thickness the corresponding factors are, respectively, 1·6 and 1·2. These factors were arrived at as a result of tests on concrete block walls but the principle of such an allowance is confirmed by the theoretical studies described in preceding paragraphs.

It might also be inferred from these theories that the lateral tensile stresses set up by the interaction of masonry unit and mortar would be appreciably smaller in blockwork than in brickwork and therefore that the mode of failure of blockwork in compression would tend to differ from that typically observed in brickwork, and this is borne out by observations in wall tests.

Development of materials tests. A rational consideration of masonry strength is bound to have considerable implications in relation to materials tests and indeed the main justification for such a study may be to make it possible to devise materials tests which are meaningful in terms of masonry strength. It can hardly be argued that the current materials tests, namely the standard crushing test and the mortar cube test are satisfactory in this respect. It may be felt that suggestions of bi-axial and tri-axial tests are unrealistic for practical purposes and indeed this may well be so. The picture at the moment is, however, incomplete and it is rather too early to say precisely what might in the end seem necessary. Possibly a simple cylinder test on mortar, giving the uni-axial compressive strength of the material would be suitable although it would be very desirable if test conditions were devised which would make the material of the test cylinder representative of that in the mortar joint. Preliminary studies in this direction have been reported by Plowman (18).

Various simple tensile tests have been tried out recently. The most convenient is the indirect splitting test (Fig. 2.7) but this presents difficulties with practical brick shapes (e.g. when there are perforations or frogs). A direct tensile test has also been developed at Edinburgh University (Fig. 2.8); this has the advantage of being able to deal with all kinds of bricks but requires some preparation of the specimens by gluing on plywood pads. Other forms of tests have been examined in this country by Thomas (19).

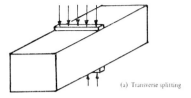

(a) Transverse splitting

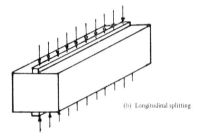

(b) Longitudinal splitting

Fig. 2.7. Indirect splitting test for tensile strength of bricks.

Determination of the true uni-axial compressive strength of brick presents a number of practical difficulties. It is quite clear that the apparent crushing strength of brick is very much a function of packing material used between the platens of the machine and test specimen. To obtain the true uni-axial compressive strength requires that the packing material should neither restrain nor augment the lateral strain of the brick under test. One method of achieving this condition, suggested by Hilsdorf (20), is to apply the load through a pair of 'brushes' each consisting of a platen with rows of projecting steel springs, stiff enough to transmit the load without buckling but not so stiff as to impose restraint on the lateral deformation of the brick. An alternative method (12) is to find a packing material which will behave in this way but it would seem probable that different packings would be required for different bricks. The simplest solution for solid bricks would be to test them on end, provided that they are sufficiently homogeneous to permit this to be done. The corresponding problem in blockwork has received very little attention so far. It is possible that in the case of blocks whose height to thickness ratio is of the order two to one, the normal compression test may be satisfactory but for relatively thicker blocks the problems are the same as for bricks.

Fig. 2.8. Tensile test apparatus for bricks.

The question of materials testing is thus still very open and will remain so until the primary problem of masonry strength criteria has been further clarified. It would appear, however, that the development of practical tests more directly related to the factors controlling masonry strength is perfectly feasible.

Effects of slenderness and eccentricity. The discussion in the previous section was concerned with the compressive strength of brickwork and blockwork as materials rather than with the strength of masonry structural elements. As is well known, the basic strength of the material in compression has to be modified to take into account the slenderness ratio of a wall or pier and the eccentricity of loading. It is of interest to examine the basis of these reduction factors as they exist in the British CP 111. Considering first the case of axially loaded walls and piers, the starting point for the derivation of a set of reduction factors for slenderness applicable to both kinds of compression member was a series of tests, carried out at the Building Research Station, on piers loaded through knife-edges so as to eliminate rotational restraint at the ends. The results obtained in these tests, as reported by Thomas (24), are shown in Fig. 2.9 together with a curve showing the reduction factors for slenderness given in the 1948 version of CP 111. It will be noted that the slope of the reduction factor curve is generally greater than that of the average of the experimental curves, implying that the load factor for piers increases with slenderness. The reason for this is, presumably, that it was thought that defects of workmanship could be greater in slender piers than in squat ones and therefore a larger safety factor was called for in the former case. The justification for a higher load factor at larger slenderness ratios must depend on the finding that there is a higher degree of scatter of results with increasing slenderness. This does not seem to be borne out by available experimental evidence although the variable load factor increasing from 5·0 to 8·4 between slenderness ratios of 6 to 27 is still incorporated in the latest set of reduction factors. The relationship between various wall test results and the latest CP 111 slenderness reduction factors is shown in Fig. 2.10. As will be observed, these are in good agreement up to a slenderness ratio of about 16 but above this the Code of Practice factors become increasingly conservative owing to the higher load factors applied at the upper end of the slenderness scale.

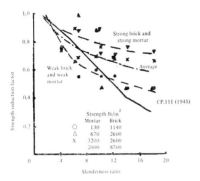

Fig. 2.9. Compressive strength of brickwork piers v. slenderness ratios for various brick and mortar strengths. (after Thomas)

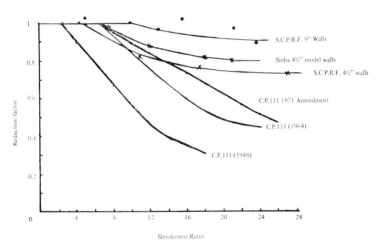

Fig. 2.10. Effect of slenderness on compressive strength of brick walls comparison with Code of Practice values.

It is also interesting to observe from Fig. 2.10 the successive revisions of the slenderness reduction factors of CP 111 published in 1964 and 1971.

Calculation of slenderness ratio, and in turn reduction factors, introduces the concept of effective height of a member. For example, the effective height of a wall which receives lateral restraint top and bottom from reinforced concrete slabs is, according to CP 111, 0·7

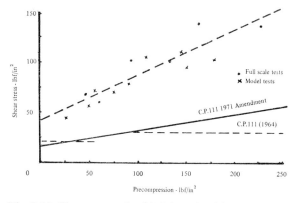

Fig. 2.11. Shear strength of brickwork with precompression.

of the actual height. This value allows for the difference between the knife edge supports used in the tests for determination of reduction factors and the 'flat end' condition which actually exists. The true effect of end conditions on the strength of masonry walls has, however, been investigated to only a very limited extent. A few tests in a specially constructed rig (25, 26) indicated that the effect of eccentric loading is considerably reduced by the presence of floor slabs, which exert a stabilising influence on the wall and also absorb part of the moment due to eccentricity.

The whole question of reduction factors, effective heights and boundary conditions is obviously of fundamental importance and would appear to be in need of further research.

2.3.3. Strength of masonry in combined compression and shear

The strength of brickwork and blockwork in shear. The strength of brickwork in combined compression and shear is of importance in relation to the resistance of load bearing wall buildings to lateral forces. It has again been studied on a phenomenological basis and although sufficient is known for the definition of permissible stresses the actual mechanism of failure of masonry under this stress condition is only partially understood. The results of tests on large scale (21, 22), and model (23) brickwork panels under combined compression and shear are summarised in the diagram shown in Fig. 2.11.

Similar results have been obtained from tests on small 'couplet' and 'triplet' brick specimens and also for solid concrete blockwork. Examination of this diagram shows that for solid brick and blockwork there is a Coulomb type of relationship between shear strength and precompression, i.e. there is an initial shear strength dependent on adhesion between the bricks and mortar augmented by a frictional component proportional to the precompression.

The strength of perforated or double frogged brickwork in shear. Brickwork built of double frogged or perforated bricks behave in a somewhat different manner at low precompressions, as the mechanical key produced by mortar entering the frogs or perforations results in failure according to the maximum tensile strength criterion down to zero precompression. Experimental results reported by Polyakov (27) indicate that the shear strength of brickwork built with perforated bricks at low precompressions is considerably higher than that built of wire cut bricks.

The diagonal tensile strength of brickwork has been studied (28) by carrying out tests on disc specimens, 25 in diameter cut from full scale brickwork and tested under diametral load with the coursing at 45° to the line of load. The stress condition produced by this arrangement is almost uniform tensile stress at 45° to the bed joint of the brickwork. Results of a large number of tests of this kind have given an empirical value of the diagonal tensile strength:

$$f_t = 2 . \sqrt{f_m}$$

where f_m is the average compressive strength of the brickwork as determined by prism tests. This indicates that the failure of perforated and double frogged brickwork will be a function of its compressive strength which is not the case with wire-cut brickwork. The strength of brick masonry in which a mechanical key exists between bricks and mortar under compressive and shear loading has not been explored to the same extent as wirecut brickwork and its behaviour at higher precompression is not known.

2.3.4. The strength of masonry in flexure

The tensile strength of brickwork and blockwork. Tensile stresses in masonry may arise as a result of either in-plane or transverse bending. In the case of in-plane stressing, tension is developed across the bed

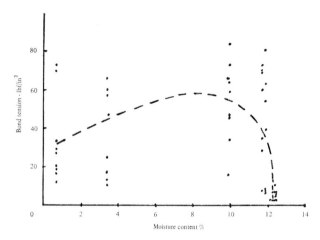

Fig. 2.12. Relationship between moisture content of brick and bond tension of brick masonry couplets. (after Sinha)

joints of the masonry and the strength is dependent on adhesion between the unit and mortar. There appear to be few systematic investigations of the factors influencing the tensile bond strength of brickwork but some work has been done by Sinha (29) on small specimens which indicates (Fig. 2.12) the extreme variability of tensile bond strength and the fact that very poor tensile bond strength is obtained between saturated bricks. Other workers have carried out tests of a similar nature, for example on crossed brick specimens, and Mason (30) has recently made a study of the tensile strength of brickwork in relation to unreinforced brickwork beams. This work indicates that there should be little practical difficulty in achieving brickwork tensile strengths of the order of 100–200 lbf/in².

The transverse flexural strength of brickwork is also controlled by tensile stress. When the bending moments are such as to cause tension across the bed joints the ultimate tensile stress is probably the same as in direct tension but the strength is likely to be higher when the bending moment is in a plane parallel to the coursing as in this case the mortar beds will be stressed as plates and the strength will not be entirely dependent on tensile adhesion between bricks and mortar.

Flexural strength has been investigated only to a limited extent (31) but the matter has become of some importance in connection with the design of brickwork infil panels which may in future be designed by yield line methods. A good deal of work will have to be done to establish strength values and measures of variability. This would seem possible using prism and wallette specimens.

Beyond this fairly simple approach, it would seem possible that a detailed study of the nature of the brick-mortar bond might make it possible to achieve more consistent adhesion and give some direction to the search for improved mortars. Very high strength mortars have been developed in the United States but are not suitable for general site work. Organic additives for brickwork mortars are under develop-ment in this country and it is hoped that these may lead to brickwork with reliable tensile properties.

The transverse strength of masonry panels. The resistance of brickwork panels to lateral pressure has received a good deal of attention during the past year or two, firstly, as a factor in determining the suscepti-bility of brickwork buildings to accidental damage and secondly, as a result of the increased wind loadings specified for buildings in the recent revision of CP 111, Chapter V. There are two aspects of the problem, according to the presence or absence of significant vertical precompression on the panel under consideration. In the first case, lateral strength is mainly dependent on a form of arching action in which a resisting moment is provided by the vertical compressive force, whilst, in the second case, resistance is dependent on the flexural strength of the masonry. The two cases will be discussed separately and, although research work is still incomplete, enough is known to give a preliminary indication of the final results.

The behaviour of strip walls with precompression has been ex-tensively studied by the British Ceramic Research Association (BCRA) and at Edinburgh University. Preliminary tests suggested that the mode of failure of a wall of this type was as indicated in Fig. 2.13: the wall fails by the development of horizontal cracks at mid-height and at the top and bottom of the panel. At the moment of failure the panel behaves as a flat three pinned arch (Fig. 2.13). Statical considerations give for the ultimate lateral pressure:

$$p_a = \frac{8\sigma_c \cdot t^2}{h^2}$$

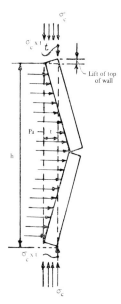

Fig. 2.13. Strip of wall with precompression σ_c at failure under lateral pressure p_a.

with the meaning of symbols given in Fig. 2.13. Comparison between the results of this elementary analysis and test results for various walls reported by BCRA (32) is shown in Fig. 2.14. Points are also shown from a series of tests carried out in an experimental building at Edinburgh (33). It will be seen that the simple arching formula gives a fair approximation to the measured wall strengths, which up to about 180 lbf/in² precompression, somewhat exceed the theoretical values. At higher precompressions the wall strengths tend to fall off as a result of compression of the material in the wall. A more exact analysis has been carried out by Morton (34) which takes this into account and which reproduces the experimental results with considerable accuracy.

The BCRA tests were carried out in a wall test frame and were subject to certain limits as to the length of wall which would be accommodated. The Edinburgh University tests were carried out by building the test panels in the ground floor of an experimental five storey building so that walls up to 16 ft long could be tested with boundary conditions representative of those existing in an actual

building. Tests were carried out on walls having one and two returns
and on 9 in thick strip walls, the results of which were in reasonable
agreement with those tested at BCRA. These tests in fact showed
somewhat higher failure loads than the wall frame tests; this was
almost certainly due to the fact that the upward movement of the top
of the test wall at the point of failure mobilised an additional vertical
loading resulting from the elastic deformation of the building structure within which the walls were built. The remaining tests in the
Edinburgh series were on $10\frac{1}{2}$ in cavity walls which behaved as single
leaf $4\frac{1}{2}$ in walls under the conditions of the test. It was found that the
effect of returns on the lateral strength of walls could be summarised
as follows:

Failure pressure $= k.p_a$ (where p_a is the ultimate pressure for a strip
wall by arching theory.)

L/H		= 0·5	1·0	2·0	3·0
One return	$k=$	3·0	1·5	1·0	1·0
Two returns	$k=$	6·0	3·0	1·5	1·0

L — length of wall   H — height of wall

These figures are intended to give a provisional indication of the
strength of this type of element and may be subject to some modification in the light of further research. Notwithstanding this quali-
fication, the order of resistance of brickwork walls to lateral pressure
has been reliably established and the effect of returns is clearly shown.
Within the normal range of precompressions it will be noted that the
lateral strength is almost independent of material properties which
also do not enter into the simple arching formula. The final observation that might be made is that the experimental results in Fig. 2.14
are appreciably higher than the theoretical line at low precompressions.
This is to be expected, as there will be some resistance resulting from
the tensile strength of the brickwork and when the precompression is
small this component will predominate.

The transverse strength of non-load-bearing panels. The condition of
zero precompression is that which obtains in infil walls and in walls of
low-rise construction or in the upper floors of multi-storey buildings.

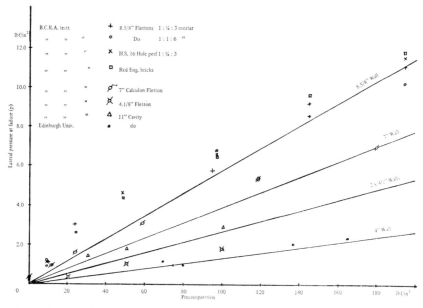

Fig. 2.14. Lateral strength of strip walls with precompression: experimental and theoretical values.

This type of element is at present under investigation but it would seem from the results of tests already available (35) that the resistance of walls of this kind, assuming that they are not confined within a frame giving rise to arching effects, could be calculated by some variant of the yield line method used for reinforced concrete slabs. Fig. 2.15 shows the typical failure pattern in a model brickwork test wall simply supported on four edges. Comparison of a few model test results with the standard yield line solution, assuming that the moment of resistance is the same for bending about horizontal and vertical axes, indicates that this gives a conservative estimate of the panel strength. As might be expected from previous studies of brickwork tensile strength, there is a considerable scatter of experimental results as compared with the strength of panels with precompression. The problem resolves itself therefore into that of ensuring predictable values of brickwork tensile strength.

Comparable work on blockwork panels has yet to be carried out in

Fig. 2.15. Failure pattern in a model brickwork panel supported on four sides, loaded by lateral pressure.

this country and very little information appears to be available from elsewhere. It is to be expected, however, that similar results will be found for this type of masonry as for brickwork.

2.4. WIND LOAD ANALYSIS OF MULTI-STOREY MASONRY STRUCTURES

Wind loading is frequently a serious factor in the structural analysis of multi-storey buildings, particularly following the introduction of

Fig. 2.16. Five storey experimental cross-wall structure.

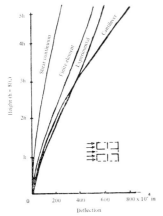

Fig. 2.17. Comparison of experimental and theoretical deflections of full scale cross-wall structure.

Experimental ▲	-75	+35	-85	+ 42	lbf/in²
Experimental + DL	-8	+102	-18	+ 109	"
Theoretical	-97	+444	-79	- 107	"
Theoretical + DL	-30	+811	-12	+ 164	"

Fig. 2.18. Comparison between measured and calculated vertical stresses for lateral loading and for lateral loading + 67 lbf/in² dead load. Average shear stress 18 lbf/in² in brickwork, corresponding to design wind load under CP3, Ch. V. (1970).

the 1970 version of CP 3, Chapter V. It is, therefore, important to have accurate information about the behaviour of masonry structures under lateral loading and about the accuracy of possible methods of analysis. To this end, tests on model and full-scale brickwork structures and on a model scale concrete block structure has been carried out at Edinburgh University (36). Figure 2.16 shows a full-scale test on a brickwork cross-wall structure carried out as part of this programme.

Various methods exist for the lateral load analysis of interconnected wall structures ranging from the elementary approach in which the wind moment is divided between the walls, treated as cantilevers, in proportion to their flexural rigidities, to rather sophisticated finite element calculations using a computer. Investigations suggest that the need for refined analysis can be established by first carrying out approximate calculations based on the simple interconnected cantilever method as this method will always over-estimate deflections due to lateral loads. If further analysis is required the method developed by Benjamin (37) may be used. This is based on the concept of walls interconnected by rigid diaphragms and takes into account both shear and flexural deformations. Other theories examined included the wide column frame analogy and the shear continuum methods. It was found, however, that both these methods considerably over-estimated the stiffness of the structure. Some indication of the correspondence between theoretical and experimental results for the full-scale brickwork structure shown in Fig. 2.16 can be obtained from Fig. 2.17. Attempts to calculate stresses in this brickwork structure (as deduced from strain measurements) have been somewhat less successful, as may be seen from the results given in Fig. 2.18. The situation in this respect is, however, probably not greatly different from what would be found in structures built of other materials if these were to be tested in the same way. Although great accuracy is not to be expected in stress calculations, it is certainly feasible, having regard to current load factors, to proceed with confidence to the design of masonry structures for wind loading by available methods. It is to be expected however, as a result of further study and research, that greater accuracy will soon be attainable in this aspect of design.

2.5. DESIGN FOR ACCIDENTAL DAMAGE

2.5.1. The emergence of the problem

As a consequence of the Ronan Point accident, much attention has been devoted to assessing the susceptibility of masonry buildings to damage of the kind which occurred at Ronan Point, following a gas explosion or other serious incident. Investigations have followed three distinct lines: firstly, an attempt to gather information about the incidence of gas explosions in actual buildings, their severity and effects; secondly, experiments aimed at investigating the resistance of brickwork buildings to explosions and to the study of means of preventing extensive failure of a structure which has suffered local damage; finally, studies concerned with the characteristics of gas explosions. The Ronan Point Inquiry and the discussion which followed it revealed a disconcerting lack of knowledge about any of these problems which subsequent research work has only partially remedied. Nevertheless, a start has been made and it is to be expected that in due course an adequate body of knowledge will become available for the purposes of structural design.

2.5.2. The resistance of brickwork to gas explosions

This article is directly concerned only with the second aspect of the accidental damage problem, namely with the resistance of masonry to lateral forces or pressures and with the means of preventing catastrophic collapse of a structure which has suffered local damage. The question of the transverse strength of brickwork panels has been discussed in Section 2.3.4, and it is appropriate at this point to refer to the important work on gas explosions in a brickwork building carried out by the British Ceramic Research Association. These experiments, which have been described fully elsewhere (38), led to a number of interesting conclusions including the observation that a $10\frac{1}{2}$ in cavity wall with an estimated 31 lbf/in² (213·7 kN/m²) precompression and with typical boundary conditions withstood a pressure of about 3·3 lbf/in² (22·8 kN/m²) before failure. Allowing for the effects of returns, this is consistent with the strength to be expected as a result of the static tests referred to in Section 2.3.4. It is also interesting to note that although this cavity wall was damaged, it did not in fact collapse and was still capable of accepting vertical loads.

A second, and quite crucial point, established by the BCRA tests is that windows and light cladding in a building, capable of resisting a pressure of the order of 1 lbf/in² (6·9 kN/m²) provide an effective means of limiting the pressure developed in a gas explosion (referred to as 'venting'). It was also found that an explosion originating in one gas filled room and proceeding to another, would produce higher pressures in the second room than in the first due to the turbulent nature of the combustion in the latter. It is possible, therefore, that in a minority of gas explosions rather high pressures may be generated by this cascade effect, and by the combustion of gas in confined pockets. The probable incidence of explosions of this kind is at present unknown but when more information becomes available on the nature of gas explosions it may become feasible to reduce the potential danger of their occurrence by suitable attention to venting.

2.5.3. Limitation of accidental damage

The question of limiting the effects of local accidental damage has also received a good deal of attention. An *ad hoc* committee of the Institution of Structural Engineers considered the matter in 1969 and as a result, a somewhat tentative document (39) was issued to members giving advice on the basis of such information as was available at the time. This paper drew attention to the fact that it was possible to design a structure complying with the Building Regulations as they then stood which nevertheless would be susceptible to progressive collapse if one wall was severely damaged. This could take the form of a cross-wall building without spine walls the gable wall of which would be particularly vulnerable. Suggestions were made as to how this obviously unsatisfactory structure could be protected from collapse following the removal of a main load bearing wall. The suggestions of the Institution were, however, soon overtaken by an Amendment to the Building Regulations (8) which specified definite requirements for buildings of all kinds over four storeys. Very briefly, the Fifth Amendment requires that in buildings over four storeys in height failure resulting from an incident (not necessarily an explosion) must be limited to the storey of the incident, the storey above and the storey below and must not affect a plan area in excess of 750 ft^2 (71 m^2) or 15 per cent of the floor area of the storey in question. In the case of a masonry structure, it is to be assumed that this condition can be met with a reduced load factor of 1·05 if a length of load-bearing wall equal to 2·25 times the storey height is removed. If it is necessary for any element to remain intact after an incident in order to limit the damage to the specified limit, it must be designed to withstand a pressure of 5 lbf/in^2 (34·5 kN/m^2) in any direction. In calculations relating to accidental damage it is specified that structural members essential to the stability of a building, must be capable of resisting this pressure at the reduced safety factor together with dead load, one third of the live load and one third of the normal wind load.

In practice, the effect of the regulations will be that the structure above a section of wall assumed to be removed will have to be capable of cantilevering or spanning across the resulting opening with the minimum safety factor prescribed. Haseltine and Thomas have put forward a commentary on methods of achieving this result (40).

Morton, Davies and Hendry (41) have identified typical situations arising in checking stability for accidental damage and have suggested suitable methods for calculating the strength of the structure following the removal of a section of load-bearing wall.

On the practical side, two tests were carried out (42) on the experimental five storey cross-wall structure shown in Fig. 2.16 in each of which one of the main cross-walls at ground floor level was removed. The tests confirmed that the structure remained stable in this condition in the manner envisaged in the Fifth Amendment. Fig. 2.19 shows the structure after one of these tests. It may be mentioned that this structure was designed and built before the requirements for damage control were introduced. The structure was considered to be representative of good practice and was capable of meeting the new regulations without any modification.

All of these studies show that it is easily possible to meet the requirements of the Fifth Amendment without difficulty provided that the principles of sound design are observed. Methods of checking stability are available and it does not seem likely that masonry structures will be put at any serious cost disadvantage by the new regulations if the research work referred to above is taken into account.

2.6. CONCLUSION

The purpose of this article has been to review a variety of problems which have arisen in the development of masonry, and particularly brickwork structures. It will be clear to the reader that not all these problems, if indeed any of them, have been fully resolved and therefore it is to be expected that as research work proceeds, the design of masonry structures on engineering principles will be further refined. This should result in brickwork structures retaining the position they have achieved during the past ten years in the field of residential building and an expansion of blockwork construction. A full appreciation of the 'state of the art' can, of course, only be obtained by making a careful study of examples of actual buildings against the background of current knowledge and research. It is hoped that this

Fig. 2.19. Five storey cross-wall structure with main bearing wall removed on ground floor.

review will be of value in making this appreciation and in foreseeing future developments.

REFERENCES

1. JOHNSON, F. B. ed. (1969). 'Designing, Engineering and Constructing with Masonry Products'. *Proc. of Conference on Masonry Structural Systems, Austin, Texas*, 1967. (Gulf Publishing Co., Houston, Texas).
2. *Proc. Second International Brick Masonry Conference, Keele*, 1970. (British Ceramic Research Association; Stoke-on-Trent) 1971.
3. GERO, J. S. (1969). 'Prestressed Masonry—Reinforced Concrete Space Structure' *Proc. of Conference on Masonry Structural Systems, Austin, Texas*, 1967. (Gulf Publishing Co.: Houston Texas).
4. BUCKTON, G. (1971). 'Modern Development Utilising the Interaction of Deep Brick Panels and Reinforced Concrete Beams to Support Multi-Storey Construction". *Proc. Second International Brick Masonry Conference*, Keele, 1970. (BCRA: Stoke-on-Trent).
5. PLOWMAN, J. M., SUTHERLAND, R. J. M., and COUSENS, M. L. (1967). 'The Testing of Reinforced Brickwork and Concrete Slabs Forming Box Beams'. *Structural Engineer*, **45**, (11), 379–394.
6. THOMAS, K., and MARSHALL, D. (1966). 'Hamilton College: Construction of Residences in Load-bearing Brickwork'. *C.P.T.B. Tech. Note*, Vol. 1, No. 11.
7. GRIFFITHS, A., PUGSLEY, A., and SAUNDERS, O. (1968). *Report of the Inquiry into the Collapse of Flats at Ronan Point, Campden Town*, (H.M.S.O.: London).
8. 'The Building (Fifth Amendment) Regulations 1970'. Statutory Instruments, Building and Buildings, 1970, No. 109 (H.M.S.O.: London).
9. THOMAS, K. (1967). 'Essex University: Construction of Tower Blocks in Calculated Load-bearing Brickwork'. *C.P.T.B. Tech. Note*, Vol. 1, No. 12.
10. STOCKBRIDGE, J. G., and HENDRY, A. W. (1969). 'Case Studies and Critical Evaluation of Highrise, Load-bearing Brickwork in Britain', *Designing, Engineering and Constructing with Masonry Products*, Ed. Johnson pp. 427–433 (Gulf Publishing Co.: Houston, Texas).
11. FRANCIS, A. J., HORMAN, C. B., and JERREMS, L. E. (1971). 'The Effect of Joint Thickness and other Factors on the Compressive Strength of Brickwork'. *Proc. Second International Conference on Brick Masonry Structures, Keele* 1970 (B.C.R.A.: Stoke-on-Trent).
12. MORSY, E. H. (1968). *An Investigation of Mortar Properties Influencing Brickwork Strength* Ph.D. Thesis, University of Edinburgh.
13. HALLER, P. (1960). 'The Physics of the Fired Brick; Part One: Strength Properties', *Lib. Comm.* No. 929, Building Research Station, Garston, (Tr. by G. L. Cairns).
14. LENCZNER, D. (1971). 'Simple Theory of Failure for Brickwork' *Proc. Second International Conference on Brick Masonry Structures, Keele*, 1970 (B.C.R.A.: Stoke-on-Trent).
15. HILSDORF, H. K. (1969). 'An Investigation into the Failure Mechanism of Brick Masonry Loaded in Axial Compression', *Designing, Engineering and Constructing with Masonry Products*, Ed. F. B. Johnson pp. 34–41. (Gulf Publishing Co.: Houston, Texas).

16. KHOO, C. L., and HENDRY, A. W., 'Strength Tests on Brick and Mortar under Complex Stresses for the Development of a Failure Criterion for Brickwork in Compression'. *Proc. B. Ceram. Soc.,* (In press).
17. KHOO, C. L. (1972). *A Failure Criterion for Brickwork in Axial Compression.* Ph.D. Thesis. University of Edinburgh.
18. PLOWMAN, J. M. 'The Effect of Suction Rate of Bricks on the Properties of Mortar'. *Proc. B. Ceram. Soc.* (In Press).
19. THOMAS, K., and O'LEARY, D. C. (1971). 'Tensile Properties of Brick', *Proc. Second International Brick Masonry Conference, Keele,* 1970, (B.C.R.A.: Stoke-on-Trent).
20. HILSDORF, H. K. (1965). 'Investigation into the Failure Mechanism of Brick Masonry', Material prufungsamt f.d. Bauwesen Tech. Hochschule, Munich, Report No. 40.
21. SIMMS, L. G. (1964). 'The Shear Strength of Some Storey-Height Brickwork and Blockwork Walls', *C.P.T.B. Tech. Note,* Vol. 1, No. 5.
22. HENDRY, A. W. and SINHA, B. P. (1971). 'Shear Tests on Full-Scale Single-Storey Brickwork Structures', *Civil Engineering & Public Works Review,* 66, (785), 1339–44.
23. HENDRY, A. W., and SINHA,B. P. (1969). 'Racking Tests on Storey Height Shear-wall Structures with Openings, Subjected to Precompression', *Designing, Engineering* and *Constructing with Masonry Products,* Ed. Johnson, Ch. 23 (Gulf Publishing Co.: Houston, Texas).
24. THOMAS, F. G. (1953). 'The Strength of Brickwork' *Structural Engineer* XXXI (2), 35–46.
25. PRASAN, S., HENDRY, A. W., and BRADSHAW, R. E. (1965). 'Crushing Tests on Storey Height Walls 4½ in. Thick', *Proc. B. Ceram, Soc.,* No. 4, pp. 67–80.
26. BRADSHAW, R. E., and HENDRY, A. W. (1968). 'Further Crushing Tests on Storey-Height Walls 4½ in Thick. *Proc. B. Ceram. Soc.,* No. 11, pp. 25–53.
27. POLYAKOV, S. V. (1956). 'Masonry in Framed Building', *Gosudatst Vennoe Tzdatal stuo Literaure po Straitel stuu i Architekture,* Moscow (Tr. B.R.S. Publ. Nat. Lending Library for Sc. & Tech., Boston Spa).
28. 'Small Scale Specimen Testing', *Nat. Testing Programme, Prog. Rep. No.* 1 (Struct. Clay Prod. Res. Found; Geneva 111), 1964.
29. SINHA, B. P. (1967). *Model Studies Related to Load Bearing Brickwork,* Ph.D. Thesis, University of Edinburgh.
30. MASON, P. (1972). *The Strength and Behaviour of Brickwork in Flexure,* Ph.D. Thesis, University of Aston in Birmingham.
31. RYDER, J. G. (1963). 'The Use of Small Brickwork Panels for Testing Mortar', *Trans. Brit. Ceram. Soc.* 62 (8), 615–29.
32. WEST, H. W. H., HODGKINSON, R., and WEBB, W. F. 'The Resistance of Clay Brick Walls to Lateral Loading'. *Proc. B. Ceram. Soc.* (In press).
33. HENDRY, A. W., SINHA, B. P., and MAURENBRECHER, A. H. P. 'Full Scale Tests on the Lateral Strength of Brick Cavity Walls with Precompression'. *Proc. B. Ceram. Soc.* (In press).
34. HENDRY, A. W. and MORTON, J. 'A Theoretical Investigation of the Lateral Strength of Brick Walls with Precompression'. *Proc. B. Ceram. Soc.* (In Press).
35. HALLQUIST, A. (1970). 'Lateral Loads on Masonry Walls', Norwegian Building Research Institute, Reprint No. 172.
36. HENDRY, A. W. (1971). 'Wind load Analysis of Multi-Storey Brickwork Structures', *B.D.A. Research Note,* Vol. 1, No. 3.
37. BENJAMIN, J. R. (1959). *'Statically Indeterminate Structures',* pp. 205–268. (McGraw-Hill).

38. ASTBURY, N. F., WEST, H. W. H., HODGKINSON, H. R., CUBBAGE, P. A., and CLARE, R. (1970). 'Gas Explosions in Load-Bearing Brick Structures', *BCRA, Special Publication* No. 68.
39. Institution of Structural Engineers, 'Guidance on the Design of Domestic Accommodation in Load-Bearing Brickwork and Blockwork to Avoid Collapse following an Internal Explosion', RP/68/03, May, 1969.
40. HASELTINE, B. A. and THOMAS, K. (1971). 'Load-bearing Brickwork—design for the Fifth Amendment'. *BDA Technical Note*, Vol. 1, No. 3.
41. MORTON, J., DAVIES, S. R., and HENDRY, A. W. (1971). 'The Stability of Brickwork Structures Following Accidental Damage to a Major Bearing Wall or Pier', *Proc. Second International Brick Masonry Conference, Keele* 1970 (BCRA: Stoke-on-Trent)
42. SINHA, B. P., and HENDRY, A. W. (1971). 'The Stability of a Five-Storey Brickwork Cross-wall Structure Following the Removal of a Main Load-bearing Wall'. *Structural Engineer.* **49** (10), 467–474.

3
Accelerated strength testing of concrete specimens

V. M. Malhotra
Materials Engineer, Construction Materials Section,
Mineral Processing Division, Mines Branch, Department of
Energy, Mines and Resources, Ottawa, Canada

3.1. INTRODUCTION

Concrete is inherently a heterogeneous material. Its heterogeneity is partly due to the nature and origin of the materials used in its manufacture and partly due to the manner in which it is placed, compacted, and cured. The criterion for quality of concrete has traditionally been its compressive strength at 28 days. In the UK, Continental Europe and many other countries in the World, the strength is usually measured on 150 mm (6 in) cube specimens, whereas in North America 150 × 300 mm (6 × 12 in) cylinder specimens have been standardized. The origins of the compression test are historical but it has successfully served the concrete industry for the past several decades, and today concrete and 28-day compression strength test are inseparable.

About 50 years ago a waiting period of 28 days was considered satisfactory to determine the compressive strength of concrete, because Portland cements were then coarsely ground to a specific surface of about 2000 cm²/g, and hence were slow in gaining strength. This, coupled with inefficient and slow methods of concrete construction, helped in the universal adoption of the 28-day strength test. Another probable reason for its adoption was that about 90 per cent of the ultimate strength had been achieved at that age. Unfortunately, this test no longer meets the need of modern construction industry. The normal Portland cements of to-day are more finely ground to a specific surface of 3000 to 3500 cm²/g, and produce high strengths at an early age; also, special high early-strength cements are manufactured. Furthermore, the construction industry is much more efficient today than it was at the turn of the century. Multi-storeyed reinforced concrete buildings which used to take years to build are being erected in a matter of months and it is not uncommon on large hydro-electric projects to place 200 to 300 m³ (260 to 390 yd³) of concrete per hour. All this, combined with new design concepts, demand that the potential strength of concrete must be known at the earliest possible time after the concrete has been placed. The results of strength tests made at 1 and 3 days on cubes/cylinders cured under standard conditions* usually show a wide dispersion and are generally considered unreliable; some means of accelerating the strength development of concrete must be found. A reliable accelerated strength test would add immeasurably to the control of quality of concrete in the field by enabling the concrete engineer to make desired changes in the design of concrete mixes sooner, and thereby assure the elimination of substandard concrete.

This paper critically reviews the past and present research work in the field of accelerated strength testing and discusses its standardization in various countries, particularly in the UK and North America. The paper is concluded with a list of 48 pertinent references.

3.2. EARLY DEVELOPMENTS

The pioneering work in the field of accelerated strength testing of concrete was carried out in the USA in the late twenties and early thirties. One of the earliest publications on the subject was an investigation by Gerend (1) in 1927. In this study the acceleration of concrete strength was achieved by subjecting 150 × 300 mm (6 × 12 in) cylinders to a saturated steam bath at 550 to 690 kN/m² (80 to 100 lbf/in²). This obviously necessitated the use of an autoclave, and consequently the test method did not find much acceptance among engineers engaged at that time on control of quality of concrete.

The United States Bureau of Reclamation (USBR) investigated the use of an 8-hr boiling-water accelerated-strength for control of quality of concrete at Hoover Dam in 1930. The boiling of 150 × 300 mm (6 × 12 in) cylinders which had been moulded in special jackets was limited to 7 hours only and the remaining one hour was used for cooling, capping, and testing the specimens. After several years of trial, the test was considered unsatisfactory and discarded (2). The ratio of 28-day to 8-hour accelerated strength was found to vary from about 2·9 to 5·6 depending largely on the type and brand of cement used.

To the writer's knowledge, from the late thirties until recently, no significant progress in the development and use of accelerated strength tests on concrete was reported anywhere in the world.

* 23 ± 1·7°C (73·4 ± 3°F) and 100 per cent relative humidity.

3.3. CURRENT ADVANCES IN ACCELERATED STRENGTH TESTING AND ITS STANDARDIZATION

3.3.1. Research and standardization in the United Kingdom

In 1953, King (3) revived the interest in the accelerated strength testing of concrete by developing a 7-hour test using oven heat to hasten curing. In this method, the test cubes, still within their moulds, were placed in a cool oven one-half hour after casting. The temperature in the oven was then brought to 93°C (200°F) within 2 hours and maintained at this temperature for a total curing time of 6 hours. After removal from the oven, the cubes were allowed to cool for one-half hour before testing in compression. Following publication of the original method, King and his associates (4–9) published a number of papers outlining various modifications of the basic procedure.

The new test approach created a considerable interest among concrete technologists in the United Kingdom. The immediate result was the publication of a number of papers on the subject (10–14). In a test method proposed by Akroyd and Smith Gander (10), boiling water was used as the curing medium; one-half hour after casting, the test cubes were placed in a water bath at 60°C (140°F) and then brought to a boil. After 7 hours of boiling, the test specimens were removed from the water bath, cooled and tested one hour later, for a total curing cycle of $8\frac{1}{2}$ hours.

In 1961, Akroyd (15) reported the development of a new method which has now become known as the modified-boiling method. Briefly, this method consists of standard moist-curing for 24 hours, boiling in water for $3\frac{1}{2}$ hours, and testing for compression one hour later. The relative simplicity of this method has led to its wide spread acceptance in several countries. A very lively discussion (16) followed the publication of the modified-boiling method; Thompson (16) referred to the use of a hot-water-curing method in which test cubes were cured in a water bath maintained at 35°C (95°F) for 24 hours and tested immediately afterwards. The principle underlying this method is that water at 35°C (95°F) acts as an insulation, and accelerated curing is partially due to the heat generated by the hydration of cement paste. This very simple approach has found some acceptance among concrete technologists in North America. The relationship

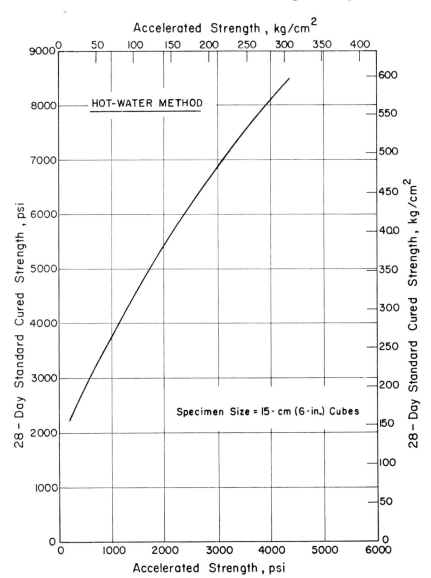

Fig. 3.1. Relationship of accelerated to 28-day strength–hot water method

between the accelerated strength and 28-day compressive strength for this method is shown in Fig. 3.1.

The developments between 1953–1958 had been followed up by the Institution of Civil Engineers, London, and in 1959 resulted in the creation of the Accelerated Testing Committee with King as its Chairman. The mission of this committee was to examine and compare various methods of control of quality of concrete with a view to evolving a reliable standard test which would be simple enough for field use and take a day or less to complete. After preliminary studies, this committee initiated a comprehensive, cooperative testing programme to develop an accelerated test method. Six leading laboratories* in the UK which have considerable experience in concrete research participated in this programme (17).

Three series of tests covering 28 different curing regimes were made. Apart from two curing regimes, when hot ovens were employed, all work was carried out in water varying in temperature from 35°C (95°F) to 100°C (212°F). Except for four curing regimes, where the initial delay time before boiling was 24 hours, all tests commenced heating cycles about $\frac{1}{2}$ hour after mixing. Testing was done $\frac{1}{2}$ hour after completion of heating.

The magnitude of the programme can be judged from the fact that for each testing regime (and there were 28 of them) three different brands of normal Portland cement and four different water/cement ratios varying from 0·40 to 0·70 were employed. Standard sand and gravel aggregates were used. The test specimens were 100 mm (4 in) cubes† with a 19 mm ($\frac{3}{4}$ in) maximum size of aggregate. A total of about 15 000 cubes were made and tested.

The Accelerated Testing Committee published its report in May 1968. The recommended test procedure is as follows:

Commence curing $\frac{1}{2}$ h after mixing
Duration of curing in water at 55°C (131°F)   24 h
Commence testing $\frac{1}{2}$ h after completion
                                                 of curing
Total curing cycle   25 h.

* The APCM Research Laboratory, Building Research Station, Construction Services Laboratory, Port of London Authority, Queen Mary College, and Road Research Laboratory.

† Some 150 mm (6 in) specimens were used, but results of these were not included in the analyses.

The relationship between standard 28-day strengths and the accelerated strengths obtained from the above test method is shown in Table 3.1. The coefficient of variation of predicted 28-day strength using single cubes was about 8·5 per cent; this value was considerably reduced if the between-batch variation was not included.

Table 3.1. *Relationship between accelerated and 28-day compressive strength**

Accelerated strength		Predicted 28-day strength	
Kgf/cm²	*lbf/in²*	*Kgf/cm²*	*lbf/in²*
70	1000	175	2490
105	1500	240	3410
140	2000	300	4260
175	2500	360	5060
210	3000	410	5800
245	3500	455	6500
280	4000	500	7120
315	4500	540	7670
350	5000	575	8150
385	5500	605	8590
420	6000	635†	9020
455	6500	660†	9420
490	7000	685†	9790
525	7500	710†	10 130

* After King *et al* (17).

† Figures given are normally only obtainable with high-strength aggregates, as it is rare to get a gravel aggregate concrete with a strength over 635 kgf/cm² (9000 lbf/ in²). They have been used in the tests by using good quality crushed granite or limestone.

Comments on the report of the British Accelerated Testing Committee. The Council of the Institution of Civil Engineers, London, has directed that the report of the Accelerated Testing Committee be sent to the Codes of Practice Committee for Civil Engineering (17). It would be up to this latter committee to translate, if it so desires, the recommendations into actual code clauses. The decision of the Codes of Practice Committee is therefore awaited with interest.

It is worth observing that no admixtures whatsoever were incorporated in any of the concrete mixes used in the inter-laboratory testing programme initiated by the Accelerated Testing Committee. It is true that some years back the use of admixtures in concrete was a typically North American procedure, but lately they are being increasingly used by the ready-mixed concrete industry in the UK. It is therefore surprising that the Committee's report makes no reference to the effect that admixtures, particularly retarders, might have on the performance of the selected test method.

It has been reported that occasionally variation in test results greater than those reported by King were found in some field applications of this method (18). This is to be expected because the nature of controls that can be exercised in the field are of a different order than those in the laboratory.

The report of the British Accelerated Testing Committee dealt only with the results of the inter-laboratory test programme, and made no reference to other methods being used by the industry; perhaps this was beyond its terms of reference. However, one such method which deserves mention is one currently being used by The Ready-Mixed Concrete (United Kingdom) Limited. The company operates about 100 ready-mixed concrete plants in the UK and produces about 20 000 yd^3 of concrete a day. The test method reported by Grant (19) has a curing cycle varying from 18 to 24 hours, depending on the field conditions (Fig. 3.2). The method seems less rigid than others but apparently satisfies the requirements of the above organization for day-to-day control of quality of concrete. The success of this method in England has led to its adoption in Australia where the parent organization has a large number of ready-mixed concrete plants (20).

3.3.2. Developments and standardization in Continental Europe

RILEM symposium. The literature search revealed that accelerated strength tests for the control of quality of concrete have been used in Europe since 1961. At present there are no official committees which have been assigned the task of standardizing the test methods in use. However, to help any such future committees, the Réunion International des Laboratoires d'Essais et de Recherches sur les Matériaux et les Constructions (RILEM), in Paris, sponsored, in 1963, an international correspondence symposium entitled: 'Accelerated Hardening of Concrete With a View to Rapid Control Test'. (21). Nine papers from six countries were published in this symposium in 1966. This is the first publication anywhere containing such a large group of papers on the subject.

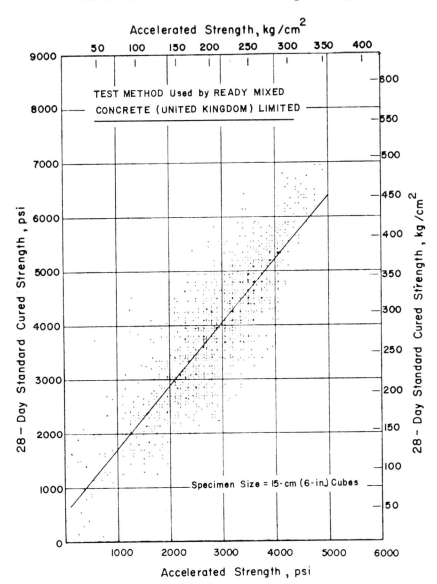

Fig. 3.2. Relationship of accelerated to 28-day strength—test method used by Ready-Mixed Concrete (United Kingdom) Limited.

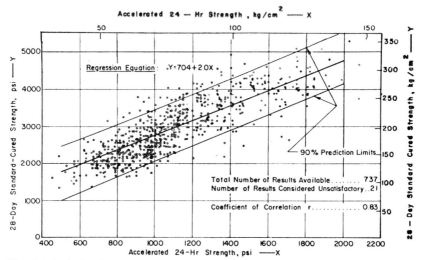

Fig. 3.3. Relationship of accelerated to 28-day strength–Snowy Mountains Authority (Australia) Method

Out of the eight contributions, only five dealt with predicting the conventional 28-day compressive strength of concrete on the basis of the results of accelerated strength tests. In this group of papers, Jarocki, Malhotra, and Vuorinen described methods using hot water as the curing medium while Malhotra and Zoldner, and Smith and Chojnacki described procedures using boiling water for accelerating the test specimens.

Jarocki (21) reported the use of accelerated strength tests for control of quality of concrete during the construction of a dam in Poland. After 12 hours of moist curing the specimens were placed in a water bath at 18° ± 2°C (65° ± 4°F), and the temperature was raised in one hour to 90°C (194°F). This temperature was maintained for five hours, then the specimens were removed from the water bath, cooled for six hours, and tested at the age of 24 hours. According to Jarocki, with the use of his curing method, the 28-day compressive strength of concrete could be estimated to within ± 7 to ± 14 per cent.

Malhotra (21) reported the results of tests carried out during the construction of hydro-electric power projects in New South Wales, Australia. The method used was the one which had been investigated by Cornwell (22) and consisted of 24-hour cycle with 21½ hours of curing in water maintained at 74°C (165°F). The field data (Figure 3.3) consisted of 737 sets of results of air-entrained concrete and demonstrated the possibility of estimating the potential compressive strength of concrete at 28 days with accuracies varying from ± 15.2 to ± 23.6 per cent (21) for mass and structural concretes made with Type II cement.

In Europe, Vuorinen (21) has been in the forefront in the use of accelerated strength tests. He has published data obtained from strength tests made during the construction of hydro-electric plants in Finland. The test method used was similar to that investigated by Cornwell (22) and Malhotra (21), except that the curing medium was hot air instead of hot water. Two sets of data consisting of 246 and 340 test results were reported and the analysis of one of these is shown in Fig. 3.4. According to Vuorinen (21) the precision of the test method is at least equal to that of 7-day test results.

Test methods used by Malhotra and Zoldners and Smith and Chojnacki will be described later.

Berio (21) concluded his general report on the symposium as follows:

'... Most researchers are looking for an accelerated hardening method that can give, a day or so after making, sufficiently exact data on the conventional strength of a concrete at 28 days. Now it seems demonstrated by the research that has been carried out up to the present that the desired result can be obtained with an average precision of ± 15 per cent, which appears to me quite acceptable.

Finally, the test cycle extended over 24 hours, in use in the laboratories that have given information as to these, differ among themselves only in non-essential details. It therefore appears possible to unify all these methods in a preliminary standardization. The preparation of these methods could well be confined to the RILEM Concrete Committee'.

Other accelerated test methods. In addition to the methods described in the RILEM symposium there are two other test methods which are being used in Europe and deserve mention. The one being used in Denmark and reported by Lichtenberg (23) is very simple indeed. The test cylinders 150×300 mm or 100×200 mm (6×12 in or 4×8 in) are cast in heavy steel moulds and immediately afterwards the moulds are lowered into a bath of boiling water. After two or three

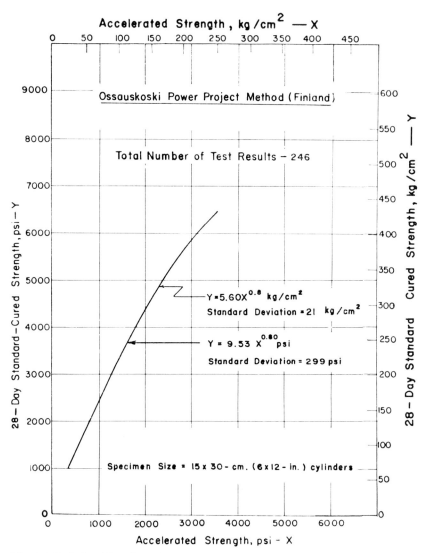

Fig. 3.4. Relationship of accelerated to 28-day Strength—Ossaukoski Power Project Method (Finland).

hours, depending on the type of admixtures used, the cylinders (still in their moulds) are removed from the boiling water and immersed for 15 minutes in water at room temperature. The cylinders are then demoulded and subjected to the normal compression test. It is claimed that the test is unaffected by aggregate type and most admixtures except certain retarders. In spite of the unorthodox nature of the test it has been used with success in Copenhagen during the past several years. The accelerated strengths are of the order of one fourth to one third of the standard 28-day strength.

The method being used in Switzerland (proposed by Z. Franjetic) is new and unusual. The tests carried out at the Swiss Federal Laboratories for Testing and Materials Research (EMPA) show that accelerated strength equivalent to conventional 28-day strengths can be achieved within 5 hours of treatment of test specimens. The details of the cycle are a trade secret but it is believed to be a thermo-pneumatic treatment of concrete. Equipment is now available, which can accommodate three 6×12 in cylinders, at a cost of about $6000 U.S. (24).

3.3.3. Development and standardization in Canada

In North America, Canada has been in the forefront of the development of accelerated strength tests. The Mines Branch of the Department of Energy, Mines and Resources, Ottawa (25–29) and the Ministry of Transportation and Communication, Ontario (30–32) have been carrying out development work in this field since 1962.

Contributions from Canada's Mines Branch. Malhotra and Zoldners (21) adopted the modified-boiling method originally proposed by Akroyd (15) for further development and study using 150×300 mm (6×12 in) cylinders. The $28\frac{1}{2}$-hour accelerated curing cycle for this method has already been described. Malhotra *et al.* (25), particularly, investigated the effect of delay time between the end of acceleration and start of testing in compression and found this to be of little consequence. Since the publication of their studies, the modified-boiling method has been adopted by a number of organizations in Canada and elsewhere (33–38) and is being experimented by others (39–40).

The wide acceptance in Canada of the above method is probably due to its relative simplicity and easily controllable curing cycle.

Field data (33) submitted to the Mines Branch by some of the

P.C.S.T.—6

organizations which are using this test have been analyzed; the regression analysis is shown in Fig. 3.5. The results of the analyses are indeed very encouraging, considering the fact that the data analyzed are for concrete made with various brands of normal Portland cement and different kinds of aggregates and admixture and have been supplied by companies from the east coast to the west coast of Canada. It is claimed (33) that with the use of the modified boiling method, the 28-day strengths can be predicted to within ± 15 per cent.

Wilson *et al.* (41) have shown that this method is equally applicable for concretes made with lightweight aggregate produced from expanded shale using the rotary kiln. The relationships between the compressive strength of accelerated-cured lightweight concrete specimens at $28\frac{1}{2}$ hours and that of standard-cured concrete at 28-days using the modified-boiling method are shown in Fig. 3.6.

Developments at the Ministry of Transportation and Communication, Ontario. Smith and Chojnacki introduced an accelerated strength test in 1963. The main features of this method, which is known as the Fixed-Set Accelerated Curing Method (FSAC), are as follows and the relationship of accelerated to 28-day strength for this method is shown in Fig. 3.7 (30).

Commencement of curing	Immediately after initial set of concrete has been reached. This means about 6 to 8 h after mixing
Duration of boiling in water	16 h
Commencement of testing	1 h after removal from boiling water
Total curing cycle	24 to 26 h.

Because of difficulty in determining the setting time of concrete and problems arising from overtime work, the Ministry of Transportation and Communication has abandoned this method in favour of an autogenous curing technique (31). With this method, part of the heat of hydration of the cement is retained by curing the concrete inside a well-insulated container, shown in Figs. 3.8 and 3.9. The resulting rise in temperature accelerates the strength development of concrete. The correlation between the accelerated strength and 28-day compressive strength for this method is shown in Fig. 3.10, with the curing cycle.

The latter method has found some acceptance in Canada.

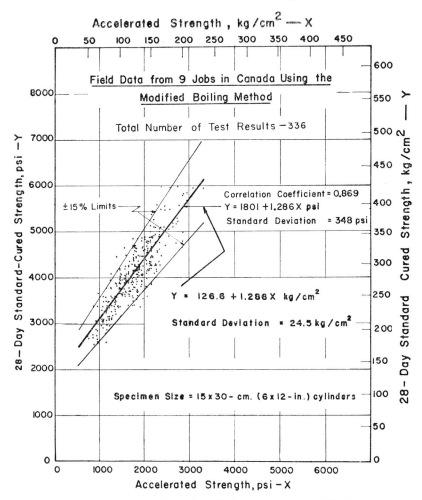

Fig. 3.5. Relationship of accelerated to 28-day strength—modified boiling method for normal weight concrete.

Standardization of the accelerated strengths tests in Canada. In 1967 a proposal was submitted by Malhotra (42) to the Canadian Standards Association (CSA) Committee A-23, 'Concrete Materials and Methods of Concrete Construction' for the incorporation of the modified boiling method in its standards. After several meetings and consider-

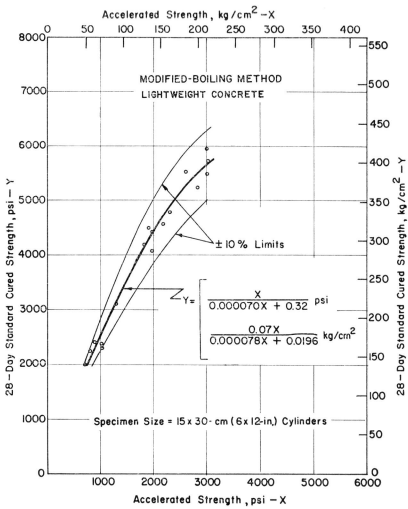

Fig. 3.6. Relationship of accelerated to 28-day strength—modified boiling method for light-weight concrete.

able deliberation the Committee, in 1970, incorporated the modified boiling, the autogenous curing and the fixed-set accelerated* curing

* In the revised standard to be issued in 1973, the fixed-set accelerated method has been deleted.

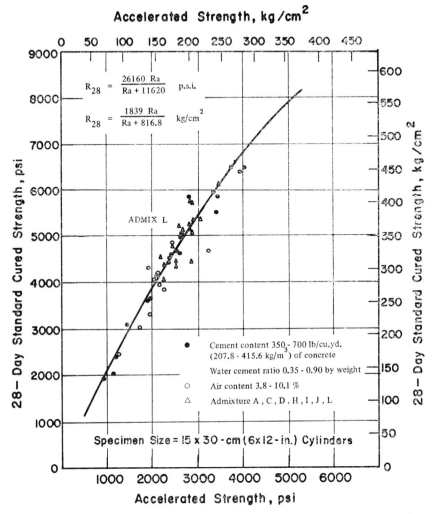

Accelerated Strength, kg/cm²

$$R_{28} = \frac{26160\ Ra}{Ra + 11620}\ \text{p.s.i.}$$

$$R_{28} = \frac{1839\ Ra}{Ra + 816.8}\ \text{kg/cm}^2$$

ADMIX L

Cement content 350 - 700 lb/cu.yd.
(207.8 - 415.6 kg/m³) of concrete

Water cement ratio 0.35 - 0.90 by weight

○   Air content 3.8 - 10.1 %

△   Admixture A , C , D , H , I , J , L

Specimen Size = 15 x 30 - cm (6x12 - in.) Cylinders

Accelerated Strength, psi

28 – Day Standard Cured Strength, psi

28 – Day Standard Cured Strength, kg /cm²

Fig. 3.7. Relationship of accelerated to 28-day strength—fixed-set accelerated curing method.

methods in its standard (43). This is a major breakthrough for the adoption of accelerated strength testing in the industry. To the writer's knowledge this was first time anywhere in the world that accelerated

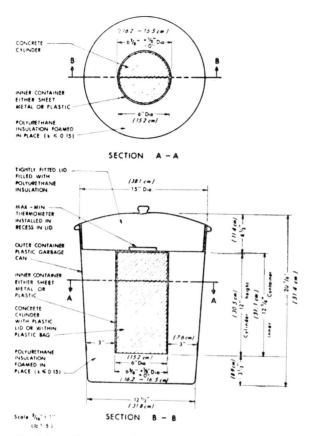

Fig. 3.8. A diagrammatic sketch of autogenous curing container.

strength tests had received recognition by a national standards committee.

3.3.4. Standardization in the USA

Testing programme undertaken by the ASTM*. The original work on the accelerated strength testing had been carried out in the USA in the late twenties and early thirties by Gerend (1) and Patch (2), but no significant development occurred again in the USA until 1963–1964. The reasons for this are not known, but probably poor correlation re-

* American Society for Testing and Materials, Philadelphia, USA.

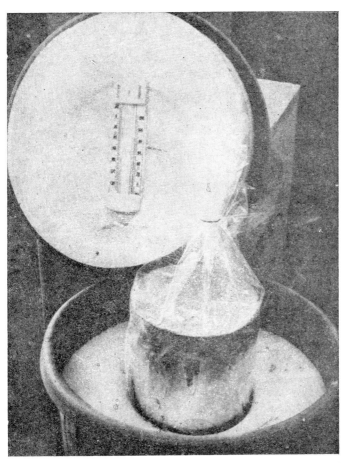

Fig. 3.9. A view of autogenous curing container receiving test cylinder.

ported by the USBR had discouraged any further work in this direction. In 1963–1964 interest was again revived in the USA by two papers which had originated in Canada and were presented at the ASTM and ACI* technical meetings in the USA (25, 30). At about the same time ASTM Committee-C9 on Concrete and Concrete Aggregates formed a subcommittee to look into the standardization

* American Concrete Institute, Detroit, USA.

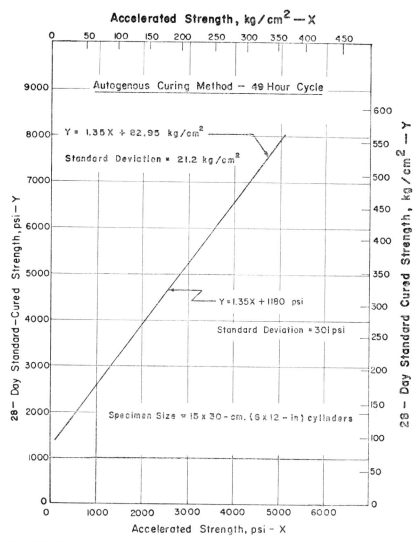

Fig. 3.10. Relationship of accelerated to 28-day strength—Autogenous curing method.

of the accelerated strength tests (31, 36). This subcommittee immediately initiated an interlaboratory testing programme to evaluate the most promising methods that were currently being used in Canada, Europe and elsewhere. Ten leading laboratories in the USA and Canada participated in this programme which, in fact, followed the work undertaken by the British Accelerating Committee several years earlier.

After reviewing the various methods in use, the subcommittee selected the following most promising methods for evaluation.

A. Hot-Water Method (16).
B. Modified-Boiling Method (25).
C. Fixed-set Accelerated Curing Procedure (30).

In addition to the above three test procedures, several other methods were also selected to be evaluated by some of the laboratories. These procedures were:

D. Hot-Water Curing for 24 hours at 55°C (131°F), at 75°C (167°F) and at 90°C (194°F).
E. Autogenous Curing Method (30).

Each method was evaluated using two types of cement, three cement contents of 155, 190 and 225 kg/m³ (450, 550, 650 lb/yd³), air-entraining agents and water reducing admixtures. Because the participating laboratories were widely separated, no standard aggregates and cements were specified; however, the maximum size of coarse aggregate was limited to 25 mm (1 in) and the specimens specified were 150 × 300 mm (6 × 12 in) cylinders.

Progress of the test programme. The interlaboratory programme was completed about three years ago. The test data were subjected to detailed statistical treatment, and from the results of the analysis the methods A, B, and E with minor modifications were incorporated in the 1971 book of ASTM standards.

3.3.5. Development in other countries

In addition to the accelerated strength tests discussed above, several other methods have been reported from Australia (44, 45, 46) India

(47) and Japan (48). These methods are somewhat similar to the methods described earlier.

3.4. CONCLUDING REMARKS

All the test methods discussed in the preceding pages have some drawbacks. Their main disadvantage is the requirement for overtime work. On large hydro-electric projects where construction is continuous, overtime work does not pose any serious problems but it can be a real handicap on small construction jobs. In addition to the overtime problem there are several other limitations of the accelerated strength tests. The test method proposed by the British Accelerated Testing Committee has yet to be used with concretes incorporating admixtures. The autogenous curing method is burdened with a long curing cycle, and test results are affected by the use of set-retarders and the initial curing temperature of concrete. The hot-water (95°F) test method, although relatively very simple, yields accelerated strengths which are not much higher than strength of cylinders cured for 24 hours under standard-curing temperatures. The fixed-set test method requires excessive overtime and introduces the determination of time-of-set of concrete—a rather erratic test in itself. Finally, the modified boiling method may need modification when used at higher altitudes, such as Denver or Mexico City, because of the lower boiling point of water.

The pace of modern-day construction demands the use of accelerated strength tests to control the quality of concrete. The availability of considerable test data over the past several years has resulted in the incorporation of these tests in the CSA and ASTM standards. Likewise, the British Accelerated Testing Committee is advocating the adoption of accelerated strength tests in their standards. All this should encourage the widespread use of accelerated strength tests in the field, and their subsequent adoption by the specification writers (36). The ultimate objectives are to use the accelerated strength tests, instead of the 28-day-compression tests, as the basis of design criteria. In this regard, the following statement from the report of the British Accelerated Testing Committee (17) should be of interest:

'The Committee takes the view that the accelerated test should not be used simply to predict the 28-day strength, but it should be used as a quality control in its own right . . .'
The Committee has also proposed accelerated strength values for use in design specifications; these are given in Table 3.2.

Table 3.2.* *Accelerated test strengths corresponding to the expected recommendations of CP114 after metrication*

Present 28-day characteristic† strength		Design strength in bending compression		Design strength in direct compression		Proposed characteristic accelerated strength	
N/mm^2	lbf/in^2	N/mm^2	lbf/in^2	N/mm^2	lbf/in^2	N/mm^2	lbf/in^2
60·0	8750‡	22·0	3210	16·50	2405	38·75	5650
52·5	7660	19·25	2810	13·45	1960	30·75	4490
45·0	6560	16·50	2410	12·40	1810	24·25	3530
37·5	5470	13·75	2010	10·30	1500	19·00	2770
30·0	4370	11·00	1605	8·25	1205	14·25	2080
22·5	3280	8·25	1205	6·20	905	10·00	1460

* After King *et al.* (17).
† The crushing strength which not more than 5 per cent of the tests fail to reach.
‡ These figures should not be used for normal gravels but only for high-strength aggregates.

REFERENCES

1. GEREND, M. S. (1927). 'Steam cured cylinders give 28-day concrete strength in 48 hours.' *Engineering New Record* **98** (7), 282–283.
2. PATCH, D. G. (1933). 'An 8-hour accelerated strength test for field concrete control'. *J. Am. Conc. Inst., Proc.* **4–5**, 318–324.
3. KING, J. W. H. (1955). 'Concrete quality control—a technique of accelerated test developed at Queen Mary College for the Port of London Authority'. *Chartered Civil Engineer* (November) p. 46–48.
4. KING, J. W. H. (1957). 'Further notes on the accelerated test for concrete.' *Chartered Civil Engineer* (May) p. 15–19.
5. KING, J. W. H. (1957). 'An accelerated test for Portland cement concrete.' *Civil Eng. & Public Works Review* (London) **52** (614), 881.
6. KING, J. W. H. (1958). 'Accelerated testing of concrete.' *50th Anniversary Conference, Institution of Structural Engineering, London*, p. 376–381 & 386–387.
7. BAKER, R. M. (1958). *The Effect of Changes in Cement and Aggregate Composition, Apparatus, and Technique, on the Reliability of the Accelerated Test For Concrete*, PhD thesis, University of London.
8. KING, J. W. H. (1960). 'Accelerated test for concrete.' *Journal of Applied Chemistry* **10**, 256–262.

9. KING, J. W. H. (1960). 'An accelerated test for the 7– and 28–day compressive strengths of concrete'. *Chemistry & Industry* **21**, 575–576.
10. AKROYD, T. N. W. and SMITH GANDER, R. G. (1956). 'Accelerated curing of concrete cubes.' *Engineering* (London) **181** (4699), 153–155.
11. ORDMAN, N. N. B. and BONDRE, N. G. (1958). 'Accelerated curing tests on concrete.' *Engineering* (London) **185** (4798), 243–245.
12. AKROYD, T. N. W. (1958). 'Accelerated curing tests on concrete.' *Engineering* (London) **185** (4811), 666–667.
13. THOMPSON, M. S. (1959). 'Accelerated curing tests on concrete.' *Engineering* (London) **187** (4866), 759.
14. THOMPSON, M. S. (1961). *The Accelerated Testing of Concrete.* MSc Tech thesis, University of Manchester.
15. AKROYD, T. N. W. (1961). 'The accelerated curing of concrete test cubes.' *J. Inst. of Civil Eng.* (*London*), *Proc.* **19**, 1–22.
16. Discussion of Ref. 15 by: M. S. Thompson, R. Cameron, J. W. H. King, P. Smith and B. Chojnacki, E. E. H. Bate, A. Bannister, G. A. Wilson, N. N. B. Ordman. *J. Inst. of Civil Eng.* (*London*), *Proc.* **21**, 678–696 (1962).
17. KING, J. W. H. *et al.* (1968). 'An accelerated test for concrete.' (A report of the Accelerated Testing Committee 1959–1967). *Inst. of Civil Eng.* (*London*) *Proc.* **40**, 125–129.
18. ANON. 'Accelerated testing of concrete.' (1969) *Concrete* (London) **3** (4), 162.
19. GRANT, T. N. (1964). 'The use of an accelerated testing method in the quality control of ready-mixed concrete.' *Proc. Symposium on Concrete Quality*, p. 172–180 (London: Cement & Concrete Association).
20. Personal communication from W. J. G. Ryan, The Ready-Mixed Concrete (Australia) Pty Ltd., 26th April 1968.
21. RILEM, (1966). 'Accelerated hardening of concrete with a view to rapid control tests.' *RILEM Bulletin* (New Series) No. 31, p. 156–209.
    The following eight papers were published in this symposium together with the general report by A. Beria.
    (i) R. Dutron, 'Quelques résultats d'essais en contribution à ce colloque.' (Some test results as a contribution to this symposium). Report from Centre National de Recherches Scientifiques et Techniques pour l'Industrie Cimentière, Bruxelles, Belgique.
    (ii) W. Jarocki, 'The rapid control of concrete strength on the base of specimens cured in hot water.' Report from the Laboratory of Concrete Technology, Instytut Techniki Budowlanej, UI, Wawelska, Poland.
    (iii) V. M. Malhotra. 'Analyses of accelerated 24-hour strengths from field tests.' Report from Department of Energy, Mines and Resources, Mines Branch, Ottawa, Ontario, Canada.
    (iv) V. M. Malhotra and N. G. Zoldners. 'Accelerated strength testing of concrete using the modified boiling method.' Report from Department of Energy, Mines and Resources, Mines Branch, Ottawa, Ontario, Canada.
    (v) N. Mihail. 'Méthode pour l'essai de la qualité des bétons.' (Method for testing the quality of concrete). Report from the Institute de Cercetari in Constructii si Economia Constructillor sos. Pantelimon Nr. 266, Bucuresti, Roumanie.
    (vi) P. Smith and B. Chojnacki. 'Accelerated strength testing of concrete cylinders in Ontario'. Report from Department of Highways, Toronto, Ontario, Canada.
    (vii) J. Vuorinen. 'Some notes on the use of accelerated curing of test specimens for

concrete quality control.' Report from Soils and Concrete Branch, Civil Engineering Department, Imatran Voima Osakeychtio, Helsinki, Finland.

(viii) H. Yokomichi and M. Hayashi. 'Influence of high temperature curing in early ages on strength of concrete.' Report from Civil Engineering Research Institute of Hokkaido Development Bureau, Japan.

22. CORNWELL, J. S. (1956). 'The reliability of the 24-hour compressive strength of accelerated-cured concrete as a basis for predicting the strength of standard-cured concrete aged 28 and 90 days.' *Construction Materials Report* No. S.M. 53. The Snowy Mountain Hydro-Electric Authority, Cooma, New South Wales, Australia.

23. LICHTENBERG, S. (1964). 'Accelererede Bétontrykprv paa 2 Timer.' *Nordisk Béton* **8** (4), 457–464.

24. Departmental communication from S. Van Wattenwyl, Intrec, Zurich, Switzerland, dated 17th January 1968.

25. MALHOTRA, V. M., ZOLDNERS, N. G. and LAPINAS, R. (1965). 'Accelerated test for determining the 28-day compressive strength of concrete.' *Transactions of the Engineering Institute of Canada*, paper No. EIC 64-CIV 10. (A paper entitled 'Reliability of an accelerated strength test of concrete' which was a summary of the above report was presented at the 1964 Fall Meeting of the American Concrete Institute, Nov. 11–13, Miami, USA.)

26. MALHOTRA, V. M. (1968). 'Analyses of compressive strengths after accelerated and normal curing of concrete on the Outardes-3 Project.' *Mines Branch Investigation Report* IR 58–60. Department of Energy, Mines and Resources, Ottawa, Canada.

27. MALHOTRA, V. M. (1969). 'Testing of low-strength concrete after standard and accelerated curing.' *Mines Branch Investigation Report* IR 69–20. Department of Energy, Mines and Resources, Ottawa, Canada.

28. MALHOTRA, V. M. (1969). 'Analyses of compressive strengths after accelerated and normal curing of concrete on the Churchill Falls Project.' *Mines Branch Investigation Report* IR 69–53. Department of Energy, Mines and Resources, Ottawa, Canada.

29. MALHOTRA, V. M., WALLACE, G. C. and PAINTER, K. (1969). 'The effect of accelerated and subsequent moist curing before boiling on compressive strength of concrete.' *Mines Branch Investigation Report.* IR 69–68. Department of Energy, Mines and Resources, Ottawa, Canada.

30. SMITH, P. and CHOJNACKI, B. (1963). 'Accelerated strength testing of concrete cylinders.' *Proc. ASTM* **63**, 1079–1101; discussion p. 1101–1104.

31. SMITH, P. and TIEDE, H. (1967). 'Earlier determination of strength potential.' *Highway Research Record* No. 210, p. 29–61; discussion p. 61–66.

32. SMITH, P. (1970). 'Quick quality testing of concrete.' *Civil Engineering* (New York). August, p. 52.

33. MALHOTRA, V. M. and ZOLDNERS, N. G. (1969). 'Some field experience in the use of an accelerated method of estimating 28-day strength of concrete.' *Am. Conc. Inst. Proc.* **66** (11), 894–897.

34. Discussion of Ref. 33 by Edward A. Abdun Nur, John A. Bickley, E. L. Howard, Rimantas Lapinas, Alejandro, G. Lopez and Sergio Z. Banera, J. Neil Mustard, Lloyd E. Rodway, Walter G. J. Ryan, Peter K. Smith, Gordon W. Spratt and Authors reply. *Am. Conc. Inst. Proc.* 67 (5), 424–434 (1970).

35. MALHOTRA, V. M. and BAUSET, R. (1970). 'Rapid estimation of concrete strength potential for the Hydro-Quebec Dams with special reference to modified-boiling method.' *Proc. Tenth International Congress on Large Dams*, Montreal, P.Q., Q. 39, R. 20, p. 415–438.

36. MALHOTRA, V. M. (1969). 'The past, present, and future of accelerated strength testing of concrete.' *Indian Concrete Journal*, **43** (9), 342–349.

37. RODWAY, L. E. (1970). *Estimation of Concrete Strength Potential from Accelerated Curing Tests.* A thesis for the Degree of Master of Engineering, Department of Civil Engineering, Calgary, Alberta.
38. LOPEZ, A. G. and BARRERA, S. Z. (1969). 'Evaluation of accelerated strength tests in quality control of concrete.' *Revista IMCYC* (Mexico City) 7 (40), 41–56.
39. MCGHEE, K. H. (1970). *Water Bath Accelerated Curing of Concrete.* (Charlottesville: Virginia Highway Research Council).
40. Personal communication from Raymundo Rivera Villarreal, University of N.L., Monterrey, Mexico, 15th January 1971.
41. WILSON, H. S., ZOLDNERS, N. G. and MALHOTRA, V. M. (1967). 'Accelerated method of predicting the twenty-eight day compressive strength of lightweight concrete.' *Proceedings RILEM Symposium on Testing and Design Methods of Lightweight Aggregate Concretes,* Budapest, p. 761–782.
42. MALHOTRA, V. M. (1967). 'A proposal for the incorporation of an accelerated curing method for strength determination of concrete in the CSA Standard A-23.' *Mines Branch Internal Report* MPI 67–65. Department of Energy, Mines and Resources, Ottawa, Canada.
43. CANADIAN STANDARDS ASSOCIATION. (1967). 'Concrete materials and methods of concrete construction.' *CSA Standard* A 23.1 and A 23.2 (Rexdale, Ontario: Canadian Standards Association).
44. BOUNDY, C. A. P. and HONDROS, G. (1964). 'Rapid field assessment of strength of concrete by accelerated curing and Schmidt Rebound Number.' *Am. Conc. Inst. Proc.* **61** (1), 77–84.
45. Discussion of Ref. 44 by V. M. Malhotra and N. G. Zoldners and D. Johnson Victor. *Am. Conc. Inst. Proc.* **61** (9), 1185–1190. (1964).
46. NICOL, T. B. (1964). 'Warragamba Dam.' *Inst. of Civil Engineers Proc.* **27**, 529.
47. DEWAN, P. L. (1963). 'A new method for predicting the compressive strength of concrete by accelerated test.' *Cement and Concrete Journal* (New Delhi) 4 (1), 348–351.
48. SOSHIRODA, T. and FUJISAWA, Y. (1968). 'Accelerated strength tests for earlier evaluation of concrete quality.' *Transaction A.I.J.* (Japan) No. 146, p. 11–12.

4

An investigation into the shear strength of glue joints as affected by gluing pressures—with particular reference to hardwoods

D. N. Nwokoye, BSc (Eng), PhD, CEng, AIWSc, MICE
The Polytechnic of Central London

4.1. Introduction
    4.1.1. Purpose and development of the investigation

4.2. Scope of experimental work
    4.2.1. Fabrication and testing of glulam beams of Iroko

4.3. Discussion of experimental results

4.4. Conclusion

4.1. INTRODUCTION

The merits of glue laminated construction largely depend on making a material that is more homogeneous, less variable and stronger than the solid wood. It is therefore of primary importance in the fabrication of structural glue laminated timber that the resulting product is at least as strong as solid wood itself and with lower or the same order of variability in strength. The efficiency of the glue joint could therefore be considered as:

$$\frac{\text{structural strength of glue joint}}{\text{structural strength of solid wood joint}} \times 100 \text{ per cent}$$

Qualitative definition of the efficiency of glued joint has been considered by some as the percentage wood failure. This is based on the percentage wood failure in the break as compared to shear failure in the glue. However, with modern structural adhesives, this criterion has proved very unreliable particularly with hardwoods. Low percentage wood failure does not necessarily mean low joint strength.

From the first definition, the general aim for efficient gluing operation is to produce joints which have above 100 per cent efficiency. This will enable full design stresses to be based on the mechanical properties of timber.

Efficient gluing operation is influenced by many factors including:

(i) The type of glue, species of timber and compatability between them with regard to thermal expansion characteristics, shrinkage properties and elastic constants which influence the stress pattern within the glue joint.

(ii) Chemical compostion of the adhesive, the extractives and pH level of the timber.

(iii) Condition of timber surface, its cleanliness and moisture content. Normally the moisture content during gluing is limited to values below 15 per cent but work by Knight and Doman (1) has shown that softwood can be effectively bonded at moisture contents of up to 25 per cent with a resorcinol resin glue.

(iv) Ambient temperature and relative humidity during fabrication.

(v) Open and closed assembly periods. These are usually specified by the glue manufacturers.

(vi) Wetability of the adhesive, uniformity of glue spread and thickness of glue line.

(vii) Magnitude and uniformity of the cramping pressure and the application time.

Of these factors, the effect of the bonding pressure on joint strength has not been clearly defined. Chugg (2) has stated that 'pressure is applied to a glued joint to maintain the surfaces making the joint in intimate contact and ensure that adhesive forms a thin, continuous film of uniform thickness.'

Knight (3) observed that 'it is traditionally stated that the object of pressure is to bring into contact the surfaces to be glued and to hold them until the adhesive has set. Pressure also forces air out of the joint and glue into the pores of the wood. It is generally implied that high pressures are needed and the belief that the thinnest glue line is the strongest supports this impression'. No quantitative definition has been given regarding the degree of contact (whether in 'atomic distance' scale or macroscopic scale) or the effect of the bonding pressure on the final strength of the joint. However Maxwell (4) has investigated the effect of wood surfaces and pressures on the shear strength of glue joints. On the influence of gluing pressure, Maxwell concluded that 'only minimum pressure would be necessary if optically smooth surfaces could be prepared for wood; just enough to squeeze the glue line down to a thin continuous layer'. This conclusion is discussed later.

4.1.1. Purpose and development of the investigation

The original purpose of the programme which led up to the experiments described was to investigate the behaviour of glued laminated beams made with tropical hardwood.

Chugg and James (5) and Chugg, Lord and Weller (6) have carried out tests on the gluability of several hardwoods species for structural use. These tests included the influence of extractives, the shear strength of the joints glued with five types of structural adhesive and also a study of delamination of glued joints after a period of 30 months exposure to the weather. The adhesives used were casein glue, resorcinol formaldehyde, urea formaldehyde and phenol formaldehyde. The glued test pieces were cramped together for not less than 16 hours nor more than 24 hours at a pressure of 150 lbf/in².

The present investigation was designed as a follow up to the above works but with essentially two objectives:

(i) To study the influence of gluing pressure on the final shear strength of the glued joints under compression shear loading.

(ii) To study the behaviour of the glue lines in laminated beams of hardwood under load conditions designed to induce flexural shear failure.

None of the investigations (5, 6) was concerned with the use or behaviour of the particular species of timber in a glued structural member. Only shear joints were tested under compression shear loading. This mode of test has been known to be influenced by several factors including width, depth and area of the glue line and by the thickness of the wood specimen. It was suspected from the investigations (5, 6) that the gluing pressure might have an influence on the final strength of the joint. Thus if only the gluing pressure is varied; all other factors, i.e. density, adhesive type, timber species, surface roughness etc. being approximately constant, any effect due to gluing pressure would be reflected on the final shear strength of the joints.

4.2 SCOPE OF EXPERIMENTAL WORK

A simple laminating jig was designed and constructed. The applied load was transmitted to the specimen through a steel beam and 1 in thick caul boards. The load was controlled by using a torque wrench which had been previously calibrated against a load cell and checked with a proving ring. In some of the tests, load cells were used directly. Since variation in frictional effect on the bolts could be expected, calibration of the torque wrench was carried out for each point (where it was used) just before laminating.

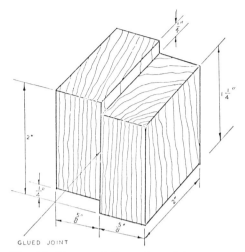

Fig. 4.1. Form and dimension of the compression shear test specimen.

A shearing test tool with a movable head suitable for attachment to a Universal Testing Machine was also designed and built.

Shear joints of Iroko were fabricated at gluing pressures of 50, 100, 150, 200, 250, 300 and 350 lbf/in² using a resorcinol resin glue with catalyst powder. The timber surfaces were planed and the glue spread was kept at an average value of 7 lbs per 100 square feet double spread. With regard to mixing, assembly periods, pressing time etc. the manufacturers specifications were strictly observed. The fabrication temperature at the laboratory was (21 ± 2°C). Follow up pressures to compensate for load relaxation were allowed. This was achieved by adjusting the pressures at intervals of 20 minutes until the load reading was constant at design value. The period of stabilisation of pressure took about 90 minutes. After the release of pressure, the joints were conditioned in a constant temperature room at a temperature of 21°C for seven days after which the block shear specimens were cut as shown in Fig. 4.1. Ten joints were prepared for each gluing pressure and each joint with a glue line area of 3 square inches was placed in the shearing tool and loaded to failure in the testing machine. The shear joint loading was applied at the rate of about 0·015 in per minute.

The moisture content of the specimens before fabrication was approximately 10 per cent. The grains of both halves of the joint were

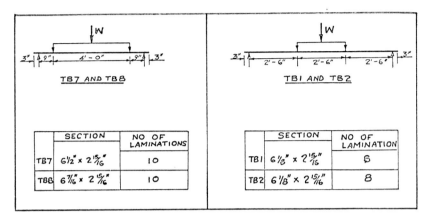

Fig. 4.2. Loading arrangement for the beams.

essentially parallel to the direction of load and the specimens were free from any visible defects.

The above test was repeated using Douglas Fir. The moisture content of the specimens varied between 10 and 11 per cent. Only five joints were tested for each gluing pressure.

In all the tests, the ultimate shear strength of the joint parallel to the grain was obtained by dividing the failing load by the glue area.

4.2.1. Fabrication and testing of glulam beams of Iroko

Test beams TB1 and TB2 were fabricated at 100 lbf/in^2 pressure. These beams were designed as pilot test beams for a wider scope of investigation. The loading arrangements were designed to induce flexural tension failure at the extreme tension fibre. These were tested on a special but simple loading frame. The load was applied by means of a hydraulic jack through a loading bridge on the beam. Load cell or proving ring (depending on the range of load required) was used to measure the applied load.

Test beams TB7 and TB8 were glued at a pressure of 250 lbf/in^2 and the loading configurations were designed to induce shear failure at the critical glue lines. These beams were tested in a transverse testing machine.

The details and loading arrangements for these beams are given in Fig. 4.2.

The rate of loading was slow and varied from beam to beam due to other information (i.e. strain gauge and dial gauge readings) required from the tests. However the effect of creep during each test was found to be negligible.

4.3. DISCUSSION OF EXPERIMENTAL RESULTS

The difficulty in the available test methods for the evaluation of shear strength of wood and of glued joints lies in the fact that:

(1) The shear stress distribution is complex and uniform shear over the glued area is never achieved. The exact nature of stress transfer across the glue line is not known.
(2) Eccentricity of load owing to the geometrical shape of the joint introduces bending stresses at the joints. With the compression shear loading where the test piece is rigidly fixed within the shear box, the induced couple together with the couple resulting from frictional forces arising from load application to the specimen is resisted by a couple created by the rigidity of the fixing.
(3) The width, depth and area of the glue and the thickness of the wood specimen influence the calculated shear strength of the joint. Jenkin (7) has pointed out that the effect of thickness is constant provided the end compressive stress parallel to grain does not exceed the proportional limit stress.

In the light of the preceding discussion it is clear that the ultimate shear stress obtained by dividing the failing load by the glue area suffices only for comparative estimates. The shear strength values would depend on the mode of test, the shape of the joint and the extent of the glue line. But if the conditions of test are kept reasonably constant, the influence of any parameters on the joint strength could be investigated. Variation in the results could be expected from any variation in friction and lateral pressure arising from the tightening of the adjusting plate screws. Ideally, to maintain constant lateral pressure (on all specimens) however small, spring loaded screws would be preferable. Care was taken to ensure that the adjusting plate just held the

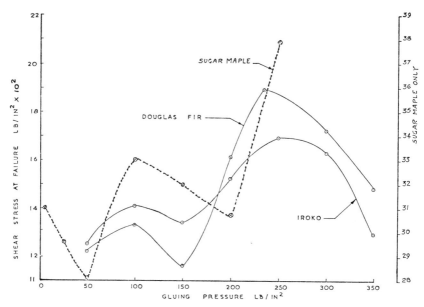

Fig. 4.3. Effect of gluing pressure on shear strength of glued joint.

specimen in position without any pre-lateral pressure being exerted on the specimen nor any gap existing between the specimen and the wall of the shear box.

Fig. 4.3 indicates that using a resorcinol resin glue and under compression shear loading and conditions of the test, the shear strength of glued joints of Iroko and of Douglas Fir, is a function of the gluing pressure. Within the range of the gluing pressures 50–350 lbf/in² the relationships show two maxima shear strength values. The ratios of the higher maximum to lower maximum shear strengths are 120 and 142 per cent for Iroko and Douglas Fir respectively.

There is an economic aspect to be considered as fabricating at the pressure (say 250 lbf/in² for Iroko) and corresponding to the higher maximum shear strength value requires a gluing jig with a load capacity $2\frac{1}{2}$ times that necessary to obtain the lower maximum shear strength. However, there are other important factors.

(1) Variability of the shear strength values.
(2) Behaviour of the glue lines in the structural assembly.

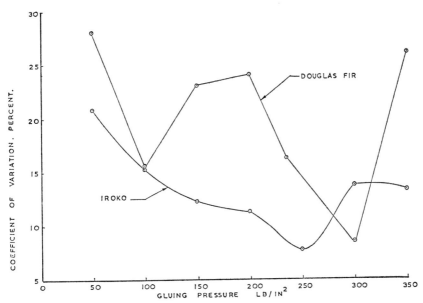

Fig. 4.4. Effect of the gluing pressure on the variation of strength of glue joint.

On the variability of the shear strength values, Fig. 4.4 shows the effect of gluing pressure on the variation of strength. These curves indicate minimum values of coefficient of variation at gluing pressure close to the higher maximum shear strength. It could be noted that if fabrication is carried out say 100 lbf/in², the final shear strength would be expected to be between those of 50 and 150 lbf/in² which are themselves lower values. But if glued at pressure of 200–250 lbf/in² the shear strength would lie on the rising part of the curves.

For the behaviour of the glue lines in the assembly test beam TB1 which was laminated at a pressure of 100 lbf/in² failed in shear at calculated shear value of 300 lbf/in². The failure was purely glue line failure running through the entire length of the beam. Test beams TB7 and TB8 failed in shear but failure was primarily in the wood. The calculated shear strength values were 1185 and 1335 lbf/in² respectively. The criterion of failure for TB7 and TB8 is consistent with the objectives of achieving joint strengths which are stronger than the wood. For these two beams the shear strength of the joints could be based on the ultimate shear strength (parallel to grain) of the timber.

It is therefore probable that the extra cost required for fabrication at the higher maximum pressure (250 lbf/in^2) could be offset by higher efficiency and overall reliability.

For these two species of Iroko and Douglas Fir the gluing pressure of 150 lbf/in^2 gives a minimum shear strength value. It is worth remembering that all the different hardwoods glued joints tested by Chugg and James (5) were fabricated at this pressure of 150 lbf/in^2. From Figs. 4.3 and 4.4 it could be deduced that 150 lbf/in^2 pressure was inadequate to give maximum efficiency for several of the hardwood species they investigated. This might well have an effect on their conclusion that 'the strength of glued joints in shear parallel to the grain increases with an increase in density reaching a maximum strength at an approximate density of 46 lb/ft^3. Beyond this figure it appears that increasing density can result in decreasing glue line strengths'. For solid timber Kitazawa (8) has established that the relationship between shear parallel to grain and specific gravity is linear. Thus higher density woods have higher shear strength values than lower density woods under the same condition of moisture. The decrease in glue line strength with increase in density above 46 lb/ft^3 seem more apparent than real. It could be that the gluing pressure of 150 lbf/in^2 does not give maximum efficiency conditions for these species. For example in Fig. 4.3, at 150 lbf/in^2 pressure, the shear strength of joints made of Douglas Fir and of Iroko are 1160 and 1340 lbf/in^2 respectively. But at 250 lbf/in^2 the corresponding values are 1870 and 1690 lbf/in^2 respectively. To base any general conclusion on the shear strength of these two species at a gluing pressure of 150 lbf/in^2 could thus be misleading.

For Iroko, Chugg and James (5) obtained shear strength value of 2353 lbf/in^2. This is quite high when compared with the values obtained from the present tests. But as already stated the shear strength obtained by dividing the failing load by the glue line area serve only as comparative estimate under the same conditions of test. The mode of test, friction, initial lateral pressure from the tightening of adjusting screws, glue line area etc, all influence the strength of the joint obtained by compression shear loading. The average glue line area in their tests was 1 in^2 as compared to 3 in^2 in the present test.

Owing to lack of knowledge on the exact nature of shear stress distribution, of stress transfer in glued wood joints and various problems associated with the mode of test, it seems preferable that for glue laminated beams, the glue joints should be tested under flexural conditions where shear is the governing factor. Factors such as transverse tension, stress transfer and strain compatability may influence the behaviour of glue lines under flexural conditions.

Maxwell's (4) work was not known to the author when this test was carried out. Maxwell concluded that only minimum pressure would be necessary if optically smooth surfaces could be prepared for wood, just enough to squeeze the glue line down to a thin continuous layer. It is not very clear how this conclusion was arrived at. Maxwell's test was carried out on Sugar Maple (grade No. 1 common) joints glued with urea formaldehyde cold setting type at gluing pressures of 5, 25, 50, 100, 150, 200 and 250 psi. For planed surfaces his result is shown as dashed lines in Fig. 4.3. This evidently indicates that the gluing pressure has a significant influence on the shear strength.

Sukapanpotharam (9) also obtained similar curves (as in this test) on the effect of gluing pressure on the shear strength of the joints tested by compression shear loading. The joints were made with resorcinol resin glue and composed of Teng, Yang, and Teng and Yang composite construction.

It is worth considering that

(i) The standard specification for fabricating structural glued laminated timber of Douglas Fir (West Coast Lumberman's Association, Portland 5, Oregaon U.S.A. 1962) stated that 'gluing pressure shall be at least 100 lb per sq. in and the minimum pressure shall assure close contact of the wood surface and provide a uniformly thin glue line'.

(ii) The production standard for structural glued laminated timber (Timber Research and Development Association) has stated that 'the cramping pressure shall be sufficient to maintain the laminations in intimate contact and ensure that adhesive forms a continuous film of even thickness throughout the whole of the cramping time. In general the pressure shall be in the order of 100 lb/sq in for softwoods and 150 lb/sq in for hardwoods or as otherwise recommended by the adhesive manufacturer who shall be given information as to the nature of the work and the service conditions to which it will be exposed'.

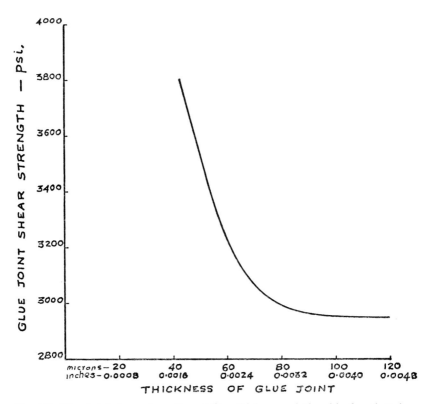

Fig. 4.5. Glue-joint shear-strength and film-thickness relationship for planed surfaces (4).

From Figs. 4.3 and 4.4 it could be seen that fabricating at 100 lbf/in² pressure gives higher shear strength value than that achieved at 150 lbf/in². Therefore gluing these species at 150 lbf/in² would not justify the extra cost in equipment. Gluing at any pressures higher than 100 lbf/in² does not necessarily mean that better efficiency conditions are operative. For Iroko, Yang (9), Teng (9) and Teng and Yang (9) composite the recommendation for 150 lbf/in² gluing pressure does not seem justified neither for economic reasons nor for gluing efficiency.

Both the above specifications stress the need for close or intimate contact of the adherends and of uniform thin glue lines. Figure 4.5 shows the relationship that exists between the thickness of a glue film and the shear strength of a joint as given by Maxwell (4). This shows that the strength diminishes rapidly to a point where the glue-film thickness approaches 80 microns (0·0032 in) beyond which it is relatively stable. This curve, could be expected to be influenced by the species of the wood and the nature of adhesive among other things. Thin glue-film could be obtained either by:

(1) Minimisation of the quantity of the glue spread applied to the surface. This will create the danger of obtaining starved joints which will give rise to very low efficiency.
(2) Increasing the cramping pressure so as to obtain the thinnest possible glue-film. The apparent effect of this would be that the higher the pressure the thinner the glue film and hence the higher the shear strength.

This is contrary to the results shown in Fig. 4.3 which shows a series of maxima and minima shear strength values at various pressures. The surface roughness of a planed timber surface could have influence on the results. Chugg (2) has given a number of surface roughness profiles for various species of timber. Wood has fibrous structure and planing produces ridges and valleys. The surface profile of planed timber therefore has the appearance of hills with peaks and valleys. The adhesive is required to fill the nooks and crannies of this rough surface and provide continuous contact between adherends. Very often air bubbles are entrapped in a thick glue line and in the surface roughness valleys. It seems therefore that for a planed timber surface the magnitude of pressure could influence the amount of the entrapped air bubbles which are expelled, the glue squeezed into the surface roughness valleys, the glue squeezed out, the extent of meshing among the asperities and valleys, smoothing down of weak asperities and uniformity of the glue film. From Maxwells (4) results, it appears that the result that gave shear strength in the region of 3800 lbf/in² (see Fig. 4.5) was that for planed surface at 250 lbf/in² cramping pressure (see Fig. 4.3).

CONCLUSION

(1) Cramping pressure has a significant influence on the shear strength and performance of glued joints of Iroko and of

Douglas Fir glued with resorcinol resin under conditions of the test. Similar effects could be expected on other species.

(2) The conclusions by Chugg and James (5), Chugg, Lord and Weller (6) are open to question since the joints were not fabricated at pressures designed to give best results for the respective species tested.

(3) A re-examination of the Specifications for cramping pressures for structural glued laminated timber is necessary.

ACKNOWLEDGEMENTS

The work described in this paper was carried out in the Department of Civil and Municipal Engineering, University College London. The author gratefully acknowledges the support interest and constructive criticisms given by the Senior Lecturer, Mr. R. H. Elvery, B Sc. (Eng.), F I C E, M I Struct E.

The author would like to express his appreciation for the contribution given by the Chief Experimental Officer, Mr D. W. Vale, Assoc Brit I R E, A M Inst E, and by the laboratory Technical Staff under his direction.

REFERENCES

1. KNIGHT, R. A. G., and DOMAN, L. S. (1967). 'The effect of moisture content at manufacture on the glue bond in laminated wood'. *Wood*, pp. 40–42 May.
2. CHUGG, W. A. (1964). *Glulam*', (London: Benn).
3. KNIGHT, R. A. G. (1952). *Adhesives for Wood*. (London: Chapman and Hall).
4. MAXWELL, J. W. (1945). 'Shear strength of glue joints as affected by wood surfaces and pressures'. *Transactions of the ASME* February.
5. CHUGG, W. A., and JAMES, P. E. (1965). *The gluability of hardwoods for structural purposes*.' Project XIV 2d. ST87, C/RR/22. Timber Research and Development Association.
6. CHUGG, W. A., LORD, A. and WELLER, G. L. (1961). *The gluability of timber species for use in glued timber structures*. Project E/RR/15. Timber Research and Development Association.
7. JENKIN, J. L. (1964). 'The ultimate shear strength of laminated timber by compression testing'. *Australian Journal of Applied Science*. Vol. 15, pp. 147–159.
8. KITAZAWA, G. (1946). *A study of adhesion in the glue lines of twenty two woods of the United States*. U.S. Tech. Pub. No. 66, State College of Forestry at Syracuse University, New York.
9. SUKAPANPOTHARAM, S. (1966). *Glue laminated timber beams of Teng and Yeng*. Thesis (No. 133) for the Degree of Master of Engineering, SEATO Graduate School of Engineering, Bangkok.

5

The American mobile home industry

Torben C. Hansen
Professor of Building Materials
Technical University of Denmark

5.1. INTRODUCTION

In 1969, the mobile home industry in the United States of America reported sales of almost 413 000 homes with a retail value of $2·5 billion. This was more than 30 per cent of all housing starts and 48 per cent of all single-family houses built in the United States in 1969, or 94 per cent of all so called low-cost housing under $15 000. An estimated 7 million people live permanently in mobile homes. The 1972 mobile home sales approached 575 000 units.

In 1970, Mr George Romney, Secretary of the US Department of Housing and Urban Development (HUD) stated: 'The cost of housing is going up faster than any other single item in the family budget. No major part of our economy is as backward as housing. Nowhere are we using less of our managerial and technical knowledge. The mobile home industry is one of the few bright spots in a gloomy housing picture. The mobile home industry pioneered the assembly line production of shelter—an idea whose time has come. It began changing the focus of the entire housing industry from construction to production'. President Richard Nixon said in an Administration Housing Goals message to Congress: 'The nation's housing goals (set at 26 million new units between 1968 and 1978) can be met, but only by including the production of mobile homes. The mobile home industry has grown so large that it can no longer be ignored'.

The mobile industry has demonstrated that assembly-line production can reduce costs by more than 50 per cent over conventional construction. Moreover, the price of mobile homes has only increased slightly over a period where conventional construction costs have sky-rocketed. The mobile home industry has broken the monopoly of building trade unions and outdated building codes which for years have prevented development of the construction industry in theUnited States. The advent of mobile homes has also upturned old concepts of taxation and financing of real estate. Mobile homes are legally classified as vehicles, not as structures. Therefore, they are by and large exempt from building codes, union restrictions and real estate taxes that apply to conventional housing.

The rapid growth of the mobile home industry represents a revolution in American housing and signals a major breakthrough in industrialized building construction. While the industry earlier operated more or less as freebooter, taking advantage of loop-holes in zoning and taxation laws and fighting resistance from local as well as state and government authorities, the statements by President Nixon and Mr. Romney show that the situation has changed. A number of laws have been passed to promote further growth of the mobile home industry and similar innovation oriented industries.

The industry has been quick to realize the tremendous size of the potential market for low-cost housing, not only in the form of mobile homes, but also modular fixed-site town houses, row houses, duplexes and high-rise buildings. The mobile home industry is getting organized to adapt its manufacturing processes to the needs of urban multi-family housing. Smaller manufacturers are combining, and outside companies, including such giants as Boise Cascade and City Investing, have bought up some of the larger factories. In Operation Breakthrough, a development program in industrialized housing, under the auspices of HUD, industry receives a helping hand in this undertaking. The development started by the mobile home industry may well lead to the breakthrough in industrialized building which is long over-due.

5.1.1. Definitions

The following basic definitions are suggested by the Mobile Homes Manufacturers Association (1).

A *mobile home* is a portable unit designed and built to be towed on its own chassis, comprised of frame and wheels, connected to utilities and designed without a permanent foundation for year-round living. A unit may contain parts that may be folded, collapsed or telescoped when being towed and expanded later to provide additional cubic capacity, as well as two or more separately towable components designed to be joined into one integral unit capable of being again separated into the components for repeated towing. Mobile units can be designed to be used for residential, commercial, educational or industrial purposes—excluding, however, travel trailers, motorized homes, pick-up coaches and camping trailers.

A/690

A mobile home should not be confused with a travel trailer which is towed by an automobile, can be operated independently of utility connections, is limited in width to 8 ft, in length to 32 ft, and is designed to be used principally as a temporary vacation dwelling.

A *mobile module* is a factory-fabricated, transportable building unit designed to be incorporated at a building site into a structure to be used for residential, commercial, educational or industrial purposes.

A *sectional home* consists of two or more mobile units, factory-fabricated and transported to the home site where they are put on a permanent foundation and joined to make a single house.

A *double-wide home* consists of two mobile units joined at the site into a single home but kept on their separate chassis for repeated towing.

Mobile homes, double-wides, sectionals and modules are transported to their sites by trucks whose movements are controlled by state highway regulations or they are shipped on railroad flat-cars.

5.1.2. Development of the mobile home industry

Mobile living has a long tradition in the United States, beginning with the covered wagons which carried many American families across the continent in the mid-19th century. The house trailer industry has been around for decades. The old trailer of the 30's and 40's was used by transients as a means of economic shelter, travelling from job to job and base to base, a necessity during the Depression and War Years. Groups gathered and 'trailer camps' grew. There were seldom any utilities in these camps, except perhaps electrical connections and the residents used community facilities. Production of trailer units increased from 1300 in 1930, upward to 60 000 in 1947. By 1949, more permanent, though still quite small, 8 ft wide, dwellings were being produced. Camps created during the immediate postwar years had high population densities per acre and no community planning. The negative impression left from the early years still results in many instances of commercial property being used for mobile home communities, instead of adequate residential property. The industry is to this day trying to erase remaining impressions of cramped quarters and squalid trailer parks, and there are still enough unsightly mobile-home locations around to keep those impressions alive. To-day, the outward appearance of the average mobile home in the average decent park is not much worse, and often considerably better, than the appearance of many single-family homes in high-density tracts.

The year 1955 marks the beginning of the mobile home as an industrialized house. A 10 ft wide mobile home unit was introduced which could not be pulled behind the family automobile. The unit was moved by a professional trucker. Consequently, moving was more expensive and as transportation costs grew during the period from 1955 to 1970, moving was done less and less frequently. Mobility started giving way to the new immobile home, which is entirely dif-

Table 5.1. *Mobile home shipments from* 1947 *to* 1969 (*from ref.* 1)

Year	Manufacturers' shipments to dealers in US	Retail sales (estimated) ($)
1969	412 690	2 496 774 500
1968	317 950	1 907 700 000
1967	240 360	1 370 052 000
1966	217 300	1 238 610 000
1965	216 470	1 212 232 000
1964	191 320	1 071 392 000
1963	150 840	862 064 000
1962	118,000	661 000 000
1961	90 200	505 000 000
1960	103 700	518 000 000
1959	120 500	602 000 000
1958	102 000	510 000 000
1957	119 300	596 000 000
1956	124 330	622 000 000
1955	111 900	462 000 000
1954	76 000	325 000 000
1953	76 900	322 000 000
1952	83 000	320 000 000
1951	67 300	248 000 000
1950	63 100	216 000 000
1949	46 200	122 000 000
1948	85 500	204 000 000
1947	60 000	146 000 000

Prior to 1947, production varied from 1300 in 1930 upward to 60 000 in 1947.
10-wide homes came into mass production in 1955.
12-wide homes came into mass production in 1962.
14-wide homes came into mass production in 1969.
The 1972 mobile home sales approached 575 000 units.

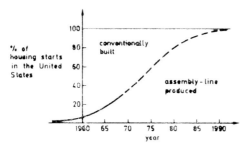

Fig. 5.1. Forecast of assembly-line produced housing.

ferent from a travel trailer. The 10 ft wide unit offered more variety of room arrangement and more privacy than the 8 ft models. Thus, it was better able to compete with conventional housing.

Table 5.1 shows that 1955 was the first year mobile home manufacturers marketed more than 100 000 units. In 1955, financial institutions started extending loans for longer periods than the usual 3 years. The post-war housing shortage was over and people could select housing by preference rather than by necessity. In early 1956, Congress authorized the Federal Housing Administration (FHA) to ensure loans of up to 60 per cent of the value of a mobile home park in order to finance new park construction.

Table 5.1 shows that sales remained around 100 000 units per year until 1962 when 12 ft wide homes came into production. From then on sales climbed steadily until 1972 when they reached 575 000 units. Some of these homes are now financed over more than 30 years. It is very significant that mobile home sales have increased markedly in the recent period of conventional housing slack and tight money.

In 1969, Savings and Loan Associations (S & L) were authorized to finance mobile homes, and the Federal Housing Administration was authorized to insure a mortgage on a mobile home up to $10 000 and 12 years, and on mobile home site developments on a 40 year basis for 90 per cent of cost instead of on a 15 year basis for 75 per cent of cost. 14 ft wide homes also came into mass production in 1969. The effect of these and other new developments indicates that 1 000 000 mobile homes or similar assembly-line produced single family homes may be produced by 1975. Another trend-forecast made by the author and presented in Fig. 5.1 indicates that by 1980, 80 per cent of all single family housing in the United States will be assembly line produced, and by 1990 conventional building construction will be completely replaced by factory production. It is interesting to notice recent interest in use of mobile modules for construction of multi-storey residential buildings. Out of four basic building systems, i.e. panel, box, componentized and column and beam, 11 out of 22 award winners in HUD's Operation Breakthrough chose the box system. If the program is successful, this could have a major impact on construction practices around the world and further speed up industrialization of building construction.

In 1969 there were 334 firms producing 10 or more units a year from 593 factory sites. In 1968, 83 firms started production while 24 failed in business. The largest manufacturer accounts for about 10 per cent of the total output. Ten companies account for 50 per cent, while the rest of the industry is fragmented among more than 300 companies. Although so far there are no real giants in the mobile home industry, this is a far greater concentration than in conventional home building, where the top 15 companies in the United States account for less than 4 per cent of the total output.

Mobile home manufacturing has traditionally been a very easy field to enter. Until recent years, most new manufacturers began with nominal capital. An investment of $25 000 was considered adequate. During 1969, a number of new manufacturers had a paid-in capital of $100 000, and several started with $150 000 or more. This reflects that it is getting much harder to succeed from scratch, and it explains why smaller manufacturers are combining or are bought up by larger companies or outsiders. Prior to 1968, very few companies had gone public, but in 1969, a total of 22 companies were publicly held and an additional 20 public companies control mobile home manufacturers.

5.2. THE MOBILE HOME

5.2.1. General characteristics and mobility

Mobile homes and travel trailers are very different to-day, although they both developed from the old house trailer. Basically, the two types of vehicles are built for different kinds of use. A mobile home is normally occupied as a permanent or semi-permanent home. A travel trailer on the other hand, is intended as a temporary dwelling for use during vacations, or other times when short-term accommodation is required.

The differing purposes of the two types of vehicles lead to some important differences in design. Mobile homes are larger, more spacious, more convenient and more luxurious than travel trailers. Separate rooms are clearly defined in mobile homes, whereas in travel trailers room definition is normally vague and living space may serve more than one purpose.

Mobile homes always include one or more complete bathrooms, and the home must be connected to utilities for use. Travel trailers have more varied sanitary facilities, ranging from none in the smaller units, to partial or complete facilities in the larger and more expensive models. Most medium and large size trailers are available in completely self-contained models where all facilities are included and no utility connections of any sort are required.

Travel trailers by design are lightweight, well-balanced, easily moved, and can be towed by a medium sized passenger automobile. Smaller travel trailers are built on a single axle with two wheels, while most medium size units and all large units are built on tandem axles with four wheels. No travel trailers are more than 8 ft in width, and few reach 40 ft in length, the legal maximum dimension for a vehicle that can be towed by a passenger automobile.

Mobile homes, though basically transportable, are moved only rarely. The types of mobile homes now being sold are ten, twelve, or fourteen feet in width, or multiples thereof and few are under 40 ft in length. The larger models are built in two or three sections which fit together to make a single home, but can be separated from each other for transportation purposes. There are in addition a variety of other plans available that offer telescopic or fold-out rooms for additional floor space. State laws require that mobile home units be moved by a professional transporter licenced by the Public Utilities Commission. Transporters' charges generally fall within 40¢ to 70¢ per mile range for each unit, depending on size, weight and type of home, and the distance of the move. These-charges however, include moving of most of an owner's furniture and personal belongings. In the future, we may well see mobile homes or modules transported by means of helicopters, or more likely by airships. A recent study, reported by Max Rynish at a meeting of the British Aeronautic Society in Feb. 1971, showed that it is feasible and economical to operate 500 m long airships capable of transporting 500 ton of payload over long distances at a speed of more than 350 km/h. A drastic reduction in the price of helium to $10 per 1000 m³ makes it economical to use safe helium rather than explosive hydrogen which was earlier used to carry the ships. Use of airships will make it economical to transport entire housing units over long distances directly from manufacturer to building site independent of existing highways. This development may well make manufacture of ready-made housing a booming business in the next decade.

5.2.2. Sizes and accommodations

95 per cent of all mobile homes are shipped from the factory, equipped with major appliances, furniture, draperies, lamps, carpeting and sanitary facilities. Optional features are available such as air-conditioning, automatic dishwashers, and garbage disposals. The homes are centrally heated by gas, oil or electric furnace. The choice of decor, i.e. Early American, French Provincial, Oriental, Mediterranean, Traditional or Contemporary is also available to the mobile home owner. Some buyers choose to custom order their mobile home, much as they would a conventional house.

Mobile homes range in area from about 600 to 2000 ft² although the bulk of sales is in models of about 1000 ft². The number of rooms

Table 5.2. *Percentage of total shipments of different sizes of mobile homes (from ref. 1)*

Width	Average length	Percentage of total shipments	
		1968	1969
ft	ft	Per cent	Per cent
8	29 to 45	·1	·5
10	45 to 60	2·2	1·1
12	54 to 65	85·9	84·2
14	50 to 70	—	2·3
Double-wides	40 to 65	8·2	8·7
Expandables	50 to 65	3·6	3·2
		100·0	100·0

Fig. 5.2. Double-wide mobile home. Standard model.

range from three to seven, excluding bathroom, but most standard models have a spacious living room, dining room, kitchen or kitchen-dinette, one or two bedrooms, and one or two bathrooms with custom designed cabinetry and closets. Mobile homes are usually displayed fully furnished, but they can be purchased unfurnished or partially furnished. Most mobile homes are built to accommodate up to four persons with comfort, but the usual household consists of two people.

Table 5.2 shows that exterior dimensions of mobile homes range from 8 ft to over 30 ft in width, and from 29 to 70 ft in length when put in place. Ten, twelve, fourteen, twenty, twenty-four and twenty-eight feet width are becoming standard, with twelve feet wides accounting for about 85 per cent of the market. As more and more states permit the passage of 14-wide homes on their highways, the market share of 14-wides is expected to grow rapidly. Lengths are somewhat less standard than widths, but 50–60 foot lengths are by far the most popular.

The exterior appearance of mobile homes is straight forward, as shown in Fig. 5.2. Many find their tin-can look plain ugly, but manu-

Fig. 5.3. Modular box-unit architecture (from M. & R. Housing Merchandiser, Nov. 1969).

facturers have found most customers unwilling to pay for improved appearance. Nevertheless, the exterior appearance keeps many potential customers from buying a mobile home and there is a growing trend toward making mobile homes appear more like the conventional houses with gabled or mansard roofs, fake shutters and fake leaded windows, sliding and skirting that gives the appearance of being a foundation. Porches or screened rooms are popular additions. It is expected that manufacturers eventually will learn to take better advantage of the special architectural possibilities which the box unit offers. Fig. 5.3 is an example.

Mobile home manufacturers are faced with a variety of design and construction problems which are somewhat similar to those involved in the building of conventional low and medium cost housing. The problem of space is acute. Retention of mobility dictates rigid length and width requirements. The problem has been solved by efficient and intelligent use of the space available. The floor plans of modern mobile homes show considerable architectural imagination. There is an emphasis on 'free flow' from area to area within the unit, and on

A.

B.

C.

Fig. 5.4. A. Floor plan for typical 12 × 60 ft, two-bedroom mobile home selling for approximately $6000.
B. Floor plan for 14 × 72 ft three-bedroom mobile home.
C. Floor plan for 24 × 60 ft double-wide mobile home.

elimination of non-utilitarian partitions chopping space into inflexible segments. There is also careful protection of privacy in areas where privacy is desired. Examples of typical floor plans are shown in Fig. 5.4. Many techniques, such as use of mirrors, create illusions of space, depth and separation of functional areas. Sliding or accordion doors are almost universal in mobile homes. Large window areas blend indoors with outdoors to add to apparent roominess. In addition, mobile home manufacturers have been ingenious in placement of fixtures and use of colour to make the most of room available. Intense competition and modern production methods within the industry keep mobile homes well ahead of conventional housing in many ways. The mobile home industry, not the builders of conventional housing, pioneered such desirable features as the counter top stove and the waist-high oven.

5.2.3. Prices, financing and operation costs

Prices of mobile homes range from $4000 to $18 000. The current average retail price is $6050 (12 ft × 60 ft overall size; 12 ft × 57 ft or 684 ft^2 living area) or about $8·85 per square foot, depending upon furnishings and appliances. By comparison, the average unfurnished site-built home costs about $16·00 per square foot, exclusive of land. The larger mobile homes ranging from 1000 to 1440 ft^2 retail from $8000 to $15 000, fully equipped and furnished. According to the US Department of Commerce, the medium price of a 1969 comparable site-built home was $25 600 including land and excluding furniture and appliances.

When financing is required it is usually arranged through the mobile home dealer who operates much like an auto dealer. He takes trade-ins, sells used homes, bargains about his prices, provides services and engages in the same kinds of financial arrangements. A used-home market has developed and there is a Blue Book similar to the annual guide to used car prices. The dealer usually originates the installment contract and then sells it to the same bank or finance company which finances his own inventory or 'floor plan' at relatively low rates. It is the financing arrangement which yields the real profit in the mobile home business. Down payments range from 20 to 30 per cent with the balance paid in monthly installments over five to ten years. Interest is usually of the 'add-on' type on which payments are computed after the interest on the entire principal at the stated rate over the life of the loan has been added. This method raises the effective interest rate to nearly double the quoted rate. These loans are so profitable that mobile homes have made large gains even under tight money conditions, while conventional housing has been hard-hit. Finance companies account for more than half the lending while small commercial banks hold nearly all the rest of the loans on mobile homes.

New federal laws enacted in 1968 and 1969 liberalized FHA regulations on mobile home and park loans and permitted federally chartered savings and loan associations to invest up to 5 per cent of their assets in chattel paper on mobile homes. Savings and loan associations may now offer 12-year maximum terms on new mobile homes and 8 years on used units. Higher yields and minimum paperwork on chattel paper make such loans very attractive to savings and loan associations.

According to the 1969 Housing Act, the Federal Housing Administration also can guarantee a mortgage on a mobile home. Basic requirements are similar to those applying to 'on-site' construction. Insurance will cover up to a maximum of $10 000 with the terms of payment not to exceed 12 years. Interest rate will vary from 8 to 10·5 per cent. The borrower shall make a minimum cash down payment of at least 5 per cent of the first $6000 of the total cost of the mobile home plus 10 per cent of any amount in excess of $6000.

It is difficult to compare the total costs of owning a mobile home with the costs of owning a conventional house. In contrast to the owner of a conventional house, the owner of a mobile home has a short-term mortgage with add-on interests, and usually rents his land. The mobile home depreciates about 20 per cent the first year, and 7 per cent per year thereafter. Although mobile homes are not taxed as real estate, they are subject to licence fees and taxes levied indirectly through the rent paid to the owner of the land as well as personal property tax. For a down payment of around $1500, a young couple can buy a $6000 fully furnished mobile home, while the down payment for a conventional home is much higher. This low initial cost is often the deciding factor. The owner of a mobile home also pays off his mortgage earlier and will later have more to spend or invest. On the other hand, the owner of a conventional house builds up equity during inflation.

Based on 1968 prices, Edwards (3) has estimated total costs of $38 000 over 30 years of buying and owning two successive 12 ft × 60 ft mobile homes with two or three bedrooms, supplied with basic furniture and the large household appliances. For comparison, the total costs of buying and owning a 3 bedroom 1000 ft^2 unfurnished house was estimated to $76 000.

Edward's summarized the advantages for the mobile home owner during 30 years. (*a*) Two new homes with new furniture and appliances. (*b*) New furnishings in each new home at year 1 and 15, and refurnishings at years 6 and 21, or new furnishings four times in 30 years. (*c*) Total down payment of $1500 compared to $4000 for the house. The first mobile home will have a market value of $1500 at the end of 15 years which equals the down payment on the second mobile home. (*d*) Savings in the bank after 30 years of about $38 000 including compounded interest, compared to $16 000 which is invested in the house, or whatever the house is worth. (*e*) An average total cost for the mobile home and park space of $106 per month, including appliances and basic furnishings, compared to a total average cost per month for the house of $213 not including appliances and furnishings. (*f*) The opportunity to live in a well-planned friendly community with facilities seldom found in areas where a $16 000 home could be bought in 1968.

The disadvantages for the mobile home owner are 720 ft^2 of living area compared to 1000 ft^2 in the house and no equity in house or land.

5.3. DESIGN AND PRODUCTION

5.3.1. Engineering design and materials

Mobile homes that come under the FHA programme must be constructed to American National Standard A 119.1 for mobile homes (4). The standards cover body and frame design and construction requirements, plumbing systems, heating systems and electrical systems. The standard for design and construction covers the minimum requirements for materials, products, equipment and workmanship needed to assure that the mobile home will provide struc-

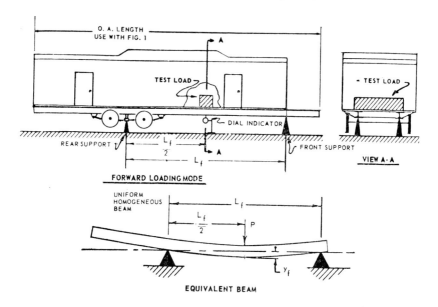

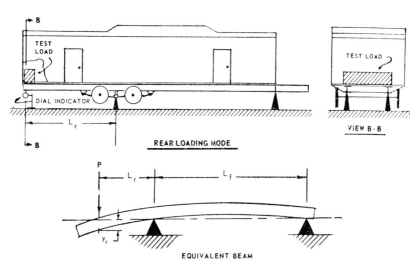

Fig. 5.5. Flexural test loading modes of mobile home structure (from ref. 4).

tural strength and rigidity, protection against corrosion, decay and insects, reasonable protection against the hazards of fire and windstorm, resistance to the elements, durability and economy of maintenance. In the following paragraphs, some of the standard requirements are discussed in order to make possible a comparison with conventional building construction.

The mobile home is designed and constructed as a completely integral structure capable of sustaining the design load requirements of the standard, and transmitting the loads to piers, foundations or wheel assembly without causing any unsafe deformation or abnormal internal movement of the structure or its integral parts on site or in transit.

The design dead loads include the weight of all permanent construction, including walls, floors, roof, partitions and fixed service equipment. Design live loads include a maximum of $25 \, lbf/ft^2$ horizontal wind load, $15 \, lbf/ft^2$ uplift, and $30 \, lbf/ft^2$ vertical downward wind and snow load. In transit, design load requirements include dead load plus $3 \, lbf/ft^2$ floor area and the super-imposed dynamic load resulting from over the road movement.

The strength and rigidity of the component parts and the integrated structure must always be determined by engineering analysis or by load tests to simulate the actual loads and conditions of application that occur both in transit and on site. However, tests for flexural rigidity must be made of each different design.

Figure 5.5 illustrates the set-up for load tests of an entire mobile home unit. First test loads of $P = 250 \, lbf$ and $500 \, lbf$ are applied front and rear as shown in Fig. 5.5 and the corresponding deflections y_f and y_r are measured. Load-deflection curves should be close to straight lines. The effective flexural rigidity $\overline{(EI)}_f$ for the forward loading mode is then calculated from eq.(1)

$$\overline{(EI)}_f = 36 \, L_f{}^3 \left(\frac{P}{y} \right)_f \, lbf/in^2 \qquad (1)$$

The minimum values for acceptable performance are given in Fig. 5.6.

Then the effective flexural rigidity $\overline{(EI)}_r$ for the rear loading mode is calculated from eq.(2)

$$\tfrac{1}{2}\overline{(EI)}_r = \frac{575}{2} \, L_r{}^3 \left(\frac{P}{y} \right) [1 + L_f/L_r] \, lbf/in^2 \qquad (2)$$

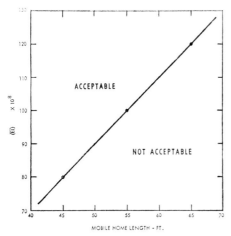

Fig. 5.6. Requirement to structural stiffness of mobile homes (from ref. 4).

The acceptable value for $\frac{1}{2}\overline{(EI)}_r$ should be within ± 30 per cent of $(EI)_f$.

The standard also specifies test procedures for roof rafters or roof trusses.

Floor assemblies are designed to support a uniform live load of 40 lbf/ft² plus the dead load of the materials. In addition, but not simultaneously, the floor must be able to support a 200 lbf concentrated load on a 2 in diameter disc at the most critical location with a maximum deflection not to exceed $\frac{1}{8}$ in relative to floor framing.

When a structural assembly is subjected to total design live and dead loads, the deflection shall not exceed L/240 for floors, L/180 for roof, ceiling and sidewalls. Every structural assembly must also be capable of sustaining its dead load plus superimposed live loads equal to $1\frac{3}{4}$ times the required live loads for a period of 12 hours without failure.

The total calculated heat loss of the living unit at outdoor design temperatures which are different in different parts of the country must not exceed 50 Btu/h ft² of the total floor area, or 375 Btu/h lineal ft of the perimeter of the space to be heated to 70°F, whichever is the greater.

While the American National Standard A 119.1 for mobile homes specifies a definite structural strength and rigidity and certain minimum requirements to heat loss, this is not so for many other important properties, such as weather-resistance, wear resistance, condensation resistance, sound insulation etc. While requirements may be stated in general terms, no definite values or testing methods are specified. The standard is prepared with an emphasis on performance as opposed to being a specification standard. Any material, appliance, installation, device, arrangement or method of construction can be used provided its performance measures up to the standard. This leaves room for a lot of experimentation and explains how the mobile home industry can be a pioneer in building construction. Approval of plans, specifications and completed mobile homes by the authority having jurisdiction under the provisions of the standard must be accompanied by a certificate of compliance from a firm or organization acceptable to the authority, by a registered professional engineer or architect or by a nationally recognized testing laboratory.

Figure 5.7 illustrates the design and materials of a typical mobile home structure. The roof is built of 2×6 in wooden rafters insulated by 2 in of glass fibre and covered with asphalt impregnated hemp board and 30-gauge galvanized steel. $\frac{1}{2}$ in ceiling panels are fastened to the wooden rafters. The walls are built of 2×2 and 2×3 in studs with $1\frac{1}{4}$ in steel bracing insulated with $\frac{5}{8}$ in glass fibre and covered with painted aluminium siding or steel siding with baked enamel finish which is easy to hose down. Chipboard or decorated easy-to-clean vinyl, formica or wooden sidewall panels are fastened internally to the wooden studs. Spaces within outside walls and ceilings are either ventilated to prevent condensation, or walls and ceilings are provided with corrosion resistant vapour barriers on the warm side. Exterior surfaces are sealed to prevent entrance of rodents. The floor is built of 10 in joist between two layers of $\frac{5}{8}$ in plywood with vinyl flooring and it is often provided with wall to wall carpeting. The undercarriage is made of welded 7 in steel channels. Windows are double-glazed and aluminium framed. Often unconventional design and materials are used. One unique floor construction developed by a small manufacturer consists of bonded cardboard honeycomb between two layers of plywood.

5.3.2. Production processes

Rowland *et al.* in ref. (5a) have made a thorough study of the production processes used in the manufacture of mobile homes.

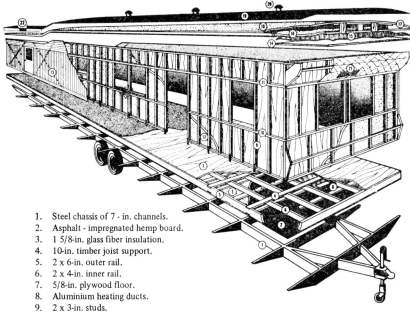

1.   Steel chassis of 7 - in. channels.
2.   Asphalt - impregnated hemp board.
3.   1 5/8-in. glass fiber insulation.
4.   10-in. timber joist support.
5.   2 x 6-in. outer rail.
6.   2 x 4-in. inner rail.
7.   5/8-in. plywood floor.
8.   Aluminium heating ducts.
9.   2 x 3-in. studs.
10 & 11.   1 x 2-in. belt rails.
12.   5/8-in. glass fiber insulation.
13.   Outside: aluminium siding; inside: panelling.
14.   1/2-in. ceiling panels or acoustic ceiling tile.
15.   Polythene vapour barrier.
16.   2-in. glass fiber insulation.
17.   Crown-trussed rafters or 2 x 6-in. rafters.
18.   Asphalt-impregnated hemp board.
19.   30-gage galvanized steel roof.
20.   Ventilating facles.
21 & 22.   Roof ventilators.

Fig. 5.7. Design and materials of mobile home (from R. Wilson: "Mobility", *Architectural Design,* May 1967).

Mobile homes are built in a process similar to the production of automobiles. Principles involved are adjacent work stations, work flow, division of labour, simultaneous operations, fixed operation sequence, interchangeable components and standardized customer options. Labour is unskilled to semi-skilled due to the narrow scope of work operations.

A manufacturer tends to conform to one of two basic methods of operation. The Indiana method is to purchase as many pre-cut and pre-assembled parts as possible. Elkhart, Indiana, is the capital of the mobile home industry, and this concentration of manufacturers has resulted in a large number of component manufacturers who supply the mobile home manufacturer in Elkhart and ship to his out-lying plants and to manufacturers who do not want to invest in the equipment necessary to process raw material. The Michigan method is to convert as much raw material as possible to finished product; it predominates when the plant is located in an isolated area to utilize a source of low cost labour.

Plants vary widely in lay-out. Some plants utilize an end-to-end assembly line some a side-by-side assembly line, and some a combi-nation of both. The flow chart in Fig. 5.8 is from a layout of a typical mobile home plant producing twelve units per day on an end-to-end line. A typical factory turning out an average of 10 to 12 units a day occupies approximately 75 000 ft².

The process involved in producing a mobile home is made up of a combination of on-line and off-line production. Off-line operations include assembly of raw materials into components in the lumber cut-ting mill, the cabinet shop, the metal shop and other sub-assembly departments.

Off-line operations. The lumber cutting mill converts raw lumber into dimensioned pieces to supply the sub-assembly stations. Material is fed into the framing jigs where it is positioned, glued, nailed or stapled, and the surface material applied for floor framing, sidewalls, endwalls and roof.

Material from the mill is also received at the cabinet shop where kitchen cabinets, vanitory units, built-in furniture, counter tops and interior partitions are fabricated.

The metal shop converts coiled steel and aluminium into formed and sized panels for ductwork, siding, roofing and trim. The metal line begins with a decoiling reel from which a continuous ribbon of metal is fed through a former, through an automatic shear that cuts it into predetermined lengths, and finally to a stacking machine where the panels are palletized for transfer to the sub-assembly department or the line. The roof metal is joined to form a single sheet to the size required and it is transferred to the line so it can be installed in one operation.

P.C.S.T.—9

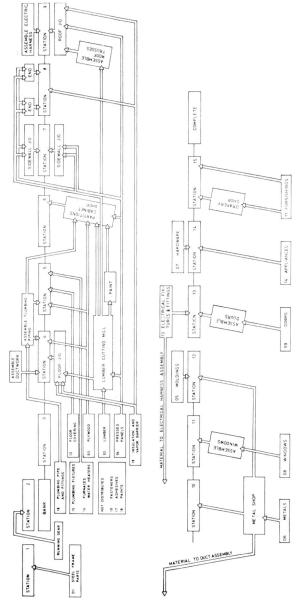

Fig. 5.8. Layout of typical mobile home plant. (from ref. 4a).

Smaller subassembly departments are duct assembly, plumbing pipe work, electrical, doors, windows etc. Plumbing pipe assemblies occurring in the floor are fed to the line, and assemblies occurring in the partitions are fed to the cabinet shop.

On-line operations. The final assembly process starts in the welding shop where steel parts are welded together to form the steel underframe. It is then moved to the next station where the running gear, tyres, wheels, axles and springs are attached and the unit is turned over. From this point on the unit moves on its own wheels. The frame is then moved into a paint room where it is spray painted. Next the steel underframe is mated to the wood floor assembly. This is a jig built in an upside down position using 2 in $\times$ 6 in joists at two foot centres or equivalent. An exterior grade fibre board is stapled to the joists for bottom weather-proofing, and a transfer mechanism picks up the floor assembly, rotates it 180° and positions it onto the steel frame where they are rag bolted together and insulation, ductwork and water supply and drain assembly are installed. Then the plywood decking is applied, secured and sanded. At the next station the plywood deck is covered with carpet or resilient flooring. This saves time on later fitting. Then the interior partitions, furnace, water heater and plumbing fixtures are installed.

The unit then moves into the next station, where the four exterior walls are positioned and secured to the floor. Moving to the next station, the wood roof assembly, built as a single unit to the size required, is crane carried from its jigs, positioned, and secured to the sidewalls. Then the rough electrical wiring is installed, insulation is completed, and the roof is sheathed with an exterior composition board. The unit then moves through stations where the aluminium exterior cladding and the metal roof are installed. Windows and exterior doors are mounted and clearances and tail lights are secured. Inside the unit, bath fixtures, installation and securing of cabinets and partitions is completed, and the finish electrical installations has begun. At the next station interior doors are hung, moulders apply all of the interior wood, plastic and chromium mouldings and electricians install fuse box, light fixtures and electrical trim. The unit then moves to the appliance bay where range, refrigerator and other appliances are installed. The plumbing lines are then inspected for leaks and the electrical system for shorts. The last station includes clean-up, touch-up, installation of furniture, drapes, and pictures and a final check.

Wet material processes are avoided on the line to eliminate drying time lag and damage to pre-installed finished surfaces. Jigs and fixtures are used for accuracy of assembly, and powered equipment is used to speed materials handling. A constant effort is made to minimize the labour required for final assembly, which results in shorter on-line cycle time—the controlling factor of a plant's volume. Audit of labour and material utilization is a continuing process, and a new material or tool is evaluated on a pure cost/benefit basis.

5.3.3. Production costs

Rowland *et al.* (5) have also made a thorough analysis of the production costs of mobile home manufacture.

Tables 5.3, 5.4 and 5.5 show an approximate distribution of labour and sales and administrative costs involved in mobile home production. Manning has been increased in the labour categories to include variable costs such as learning time, warranty work, set-up time, over-

Table 5.3. *Indirect labour costs in the manufacture of mobile homes (from ref. 5)*

INDIRECT LABOUR	Number of men	Dollars per hour	Total ($)
Plant superintendent	1	6·00	6·00
Assistent superintendent	1	5·00	5·00
Material foreman	1	3·00	3·00
Material handling	10	2·00	20·00
Tool room	2	2·50	5·00
Warehouse and inventory	5	2·00	10·00
Inspectors	2	3.00	6·00
Equipment maintenance	4	3·00	12·00
Plant cleanup	4	1·50	6·00
Product cleanup	2	1·50	3·00
Shipping foreman	1	3·00	3·00
Shipping clerk	2	2·00	4·00
Security	4	2·00	8·00
Total indirect labour	39		91·00

39 men at $91·00 per hour times 8 hours per day = $728·00 ÷ 12 units per day is $60·67 indirect labour per unit.

Table 5.4. *Direct labour costs in the manufacture of mobile homes* (*from ref.* 5)

DIRECT LABOUR Production groups	Number of men	Dollars per hour	Total ($)
Foreman	1	4·00	4·00
Group leaders	5	3·00	15·00
Welding shop	5	3·00	15·00
Frame paint shop	1	2·00	2·00
Floor frame jig	6	2·00	12·00
Sidewall and endwall jigs	14	2·00	28·00
Truss assembly	2	2·00	4·00
Roof jig	4	2·00	8·00
Stations 4-9, inclusive	50	2·00	100·00
Foreman	1	4·00	4·00
Group leaders	4	3·00	12·00
Metal shop	5	2·00	10·00
Ductwork assembly	1	2·00	2·00
Plumbing assembly	1	3·00	3·00
Electrical assembly	2	3.00	6·00
Window assembly	2	2·00	4·00
Door assembly	2	2·00	4·00
Drapery shop	4	2·00	8·00
Stations 10-15, inclusive	40	2·00	80·00
Foreman	1	4·00	4·00
Group leaders	3	3·00	9·00
Lumber cutting mill	6	2·00	12·00
Cabinet shop	7	2·00	14·00
Total direct labour	167		360·00

167 men at $360·000 per hour times 8 hours per day = £2880·00 ÷ 12 units per day is $240·00 direct labour per unit.

time and union grievance. Rate of pay is averaged and rounded from many plants surveyed.

The tables indicate that the costs of indirect and direct labour for one day of plant operation are about $3600. With a plant output of at least 12 units a day the total labour cost per mobile home is $300, or about $60 for indirect labour and $240 for direct labour. The cost for general, administration and sales averages $1125 per day based on a work year of 250 days. When at least 12 units per day are produced, this cost is under $100 per unit.

Materials costs are accounted for by cross-indexing: (a) the raw

Table 5.5. *General and administrative and sales costs in the manufacture of mobile homes (from ref. 5)*

GENERAL AND ADMINISTRATIVE AND SALES	
	Annual salary
General manager	24 000
Production manager	15 000
Secretary	6000
Industrial engineer	12 000
Draftsman	8000
Draftsman	6500
Draftsman	6500
Interior decorator	10 000
Purchasing agent	8000
Secretary	5000
Secretary	5000
Controller	10 000
Accountant	6500
Accountant	6500
Secretary	5000
Sales manager	16 000
Salesmen commissions	120 000
Total	270 000

Table 5.6. *Materials costs in the manufacture of mobile homes (from ref. 5)*

Materials cost breakdown	Cost per unit ($)
Steel underframe	400·00
Floor assembly	245·00
Cabinets and partitions	205·00
Exterior walls	170·00
Ceiling and roof assembly	120·00
Metal	240·00
Windows	105·00
Doors	110·00
Plumbing	130·00
Electrical	95·00
Appliances and furnace	345·00
Fasteners, adhesives, paints	90·00
Hardware	50·00
Mouldings	75·00
Draperies and furnishings	300·00
Total	2680·00

material category in which the material is purchased, and (b) the assembly category in which it is used. Table (5.6) shows the approximate materials content of a typical $4000 factory price mobile home according to the assembly categories. Costs include allowance for waste, obsolescence and other variables.

It is obvious that the mobile home industry gets a large discount on materials. Even a small producer of 2000–3000 mobile homes per year is a volume buyer. Suppliers to the industry find it an attractive market. The opportunity for sales volume on a large scale to a comparatively small number of manufacturers lends itself to contract selling matched by few other industries. In furnishings, the mobile home manufacturers are the largest contract buyers after the federal government. In the 70's industry purchases of steel, aluminium, plywood, lumber, appliances, furniture, carpeting and other items will exceed $2 billion a year.

Most producers of mobile homes work with minimal inventories. The tendency is to buy as many parts as possible ready-made from suppliers and the ideal is to have the day's inventory delivered in the morning before work starts and have it all used up in the evening. In any case mobile home plants try to keep on hand inventories for no more than two weeks production.

If plant production is consistent at 12 units a day, assuming a $4000 factory sales price for each unit, the combined direct and indirect labour costs per unit are about $300 or 7·5 per cent of factory sale price. Material cost is 67 per cent of factory sale price. The ratio of 7·5 per cent labour to 67 per cent material will vary with the degree of purchase of preassembled components, that is, the cost of material will rise, and the labour costs will decrease, though on a much smaller proportion. It is interesting to note that much more can be paid for the highest quality materials without a significant increase in labour content. This is not the case in conventional housing.

In addition to general and administrative and sales, overheads include payroll taxes, insurance and benefits, plant operation expense and depreciation on plant and equipment. The industry average for overheads is slightly below 15 per cent. There are hundreds of small operations whose costs do not reflect the efficiencies shown here; however lower overheads help them to maintain their competitive position.

A multi-plant operation displaces some of the overhead by supplementing manufacturing engineering, design and administration: only direct costs are reported and the balance retained by the parent company as profit contributions.

There is apparently a very high return on invested capital. However, the product is subject to a sensitive and specialized market with sales inversely proportionate to population density. This results in poor distribution characteristics, higher interest rates on shorter time loans, and a poor reflection on the product's image. This plant, with numbers based on maximum single shift production, may often operate below its maximum capacity, quickly increasing labour and overhead cost percentages.

5.3.4. Quality of mobile homes

Rowland *et al.* (5) finally studied the quality of mobile homes by inspecting a number of used homes from one to fifteen years old.

The observations of the exterior of the units indicated that the baked enamel finished light-gauge aluminium siding commonly used is rather impervious to the effects of weather and sun fading and requires little maintenance. The only disadvantage seen was denting around areas of heavy use. The roofing material, galvanized steel sheeting retained its weather seal, when maintained properly with liquid sealer. The windows, usually of small aluminium frame awning or jalousie type, operated even after severe abuse. The sub-frame supporting the box appeared to rust frequently even when it was protected with asphalt impregnated board.

The interiors of the mobile home units varied more than the exteriors. The floors in most units over two years old were in unsatisfactory condition either from heavy use or high concentration of furniture or from inferior adhesive or workmanship. The walls of prefinished plywood and composition material seems to hold up reasonably well provided they are well cared for and maintained. However, in bathrooms where moisture is a constant problem and in areas where the roof had leaked, wall panels were badly warped. The major problem with ceilings was warping due to roof leakage in poorly maintained units. The interior doors seemed to stand use well; however, the hardware appeared to be of inferior quality. The cabinetry used demonstrated a marked decline in workmanship and

Fig. 5.9. Typical mobile home park.

materials in recent years. Bathroom fixtures were standard with problems found only in ones that were not well sealed, especially around the bathtub.

In seeking to build permanent units with life spans of forty years or more using the technology of the mobile home industry, it is apparent from these observations that more durable materials should be used and that materials should be replaceable for easy repair of damage and for later remodelling.

5.4. OWNERSHIP AND OCCUPANCY

5.4.1. Mobile home parks

Mobile homes belong in a mobile home park (see Fig. 5.9) not in a back-yard or on a single site among conventional homes. When mobile homes are placed on individually owned properties in rural or small town locations, the result is less desirable.

A modern mobile home development provides a package including maintenance, landscaped lots, paved streets with curbs and side walks, adequate street lighting, off-street parking, underground utilities, laundry facilities, green areas, swimming pool, putting greens, community centre and other recreational facilities. Some have day-care centres, cable TV, man-made lakes and shopping centres.

Each home is jacked up and placed on concrete blocks which rest on a concrete slab about the size of the overall area of the home. Standard connections are provided in the foundation to the sewage, water, electricity and telephone mains, and for gas, oil, and TV antenna. It is normally up to the dealer to transport the mobile home to its site, set it up on blocks and make the necessary connections to utilities.

Currently there are approximately 15 000 mobile home parks listed in the yearly edition of Woodall's Mobile Home Park Directory (6) that rates them for appearance, facilities and management. Many more are in existence. The parks usually lie on the far perimeters of major metropolitan areas, in and around smaller population centres, and in retirement areas. Most developments built to-day have a minimum of 200 sites. The average development cost per site is $2200 to $2650, exclusive of land, and varies considerably with the facilities and amenities provided. 6 to 8 home sites per acre is considered desirable.

Park rentals vary from $30 to $90 per month with the national average for a modern development ranging between $50 and $60 per month. The potential profit for park owners is about 25 per cent a year on equity before taxes, and even more with the probable appreciation of the land. About a year is required to plan, zone, subdivide, landscape, provide utilities and build roadways for a modern mobile home park.

60 per cent occupancy is necessary to meet operating expenses. The national average vacancy rate in 1969 was 5 per cent. This indicates a shortage of adequate park sites in many parts of the country which threatens to impede the growth of mobile home sales. Developing and operating a mobile home community is now a specialized and recognized activity in the housing industry. Larger areas of land providing for larger communities are being planned as financially strong companies, and sophisticated and skilled land developers, enter the field. In the past, the industry has been selling half of a home package. The land problem must be solved in order to assure the growth of the industry. Several large mobile home manufacturers and the Mobile

Home Manufacturers Association have established park development divisions and devote money and effort to solve the land problem. At the same time, the demand for low-cost housing has started a trend toward improved zoning laws that give greater attention to the design of mobile home communities as a part of overall city planning, and many communities are beginning to lower their resistance to new well-designed mobile home parks. In 1967, park developers had a 40 per cent batting average with planning commissions. In 1969 ratings ran 75–80 per cent in their favour.

In recent years there has been a new trend toward building of mobile home subdivisions on the condominium ownership principle to provide for maintenance of community facilities.

Mobile homes make it possible to operate with dynamic city plans instead of the traditional static plans where the priority once assigned to land use often remains unchanged for a century or more. Use of mobile homes makes it possible in a constructive way temporarily to utilize land between commercial and residential districts of a city which frequently lies idle or develops slowly between the two districts. The mobile home park also makes possible intelligent interim use of land which will later be needed for other purposes. A city holding land or wishing to buy land in advance of immediate need can lease it for a mobile home park or develop and operate it as a municipal mobile home park. A long-range investor can operate a mobile home park on land while he waits for the area around it to develop before conversion for instance to a shopping centre.

It is very important that all legal and tax problems concerning development, operation and discontinuation of mobile home parks in an area be solved before the first parks are developed and that the parks are worked into a comprehensive city plan. Often this has not been done in the United States and it explains much of the dissatisfaction and resistance against mobile homes.

5.4.2. Mobile home owners

Table 5.7 shows some results of a survey of home owners conducted by the US Bureau of Census for Department of Housing and Urban Development (7).

According to the survey, the majority of owners do not buy mobile homes because they are mobile. 81 out of 100 household heads planned to continue living in their homes. Of those planning to move or sell, less than 25 per cent of them planned to move within one year, another 25 per cent would move between 1 and 3 years from the time of survey, and the remaining 50 per cent planned no moves before 3 years. Most mobile homes are never moved once they have been placed on the site.

The majority of all mobile home households have no children under 18. Half of those with children under 18 have only children under the school age of 6, generally one child. The average income of mobile home occupants is slightly below the national average. This is not surprising considering the high proportions of young people with their years of peak earnings still ahead. Many occupants of mobile homes shift to more spacious housing as their families get older and larger. The educational level is about the same for adult mobile home residents as for the general population.

Table 5.7. *Characteristics of mobile home families (from ref.* 1)

	($) Mobile home survey‡* Per cent	1967 CPS† all families‡ Per cent
Persons in household		
1	10·7	15·5
2	39·7	28·3
3	23·9	17·6
4	14·5	16·1
5	7·0	10·6
6	2·8	5·9
7	1·4	6·0
Median persons	2·49	2·85
Household composition		
2 or more persons	89·6	84·5
Husband wife	84·6	72·2
Other male head	1·3	2·7
Female head	3·6	9·6
1 person	10·7	15·5
Age groups		
Less than 35 years	49·4	23·6
35 to 54	29·4	4·04
55 to 64	11·8	16·7
65 and over	9·3	19·4

Table 5.7.—*continued.*

	Mobile home survey* 2 or more persons household head‡ Per cent	1967 CPS† all families‡ Per cent
Children's age		
None under 18	46·9	44·0
1 child under 18	26·0	17·8
2 or more under 18	27·1	38·2
None under 6	62·8	71·6
1 or more under 6	37·2	28·4
Income ($)		
4999 and under	27·6	28·2
5000 to 6999	27·2	17·8
7000 to 9999	29·4	24·4
10 000 to 14 999	13·2	20·4
15 000 or more	2·5	9·2
Median dollars	$6620	$7440
Education		
Less than 8th grade	7·5	13·2
8th through 12th grade	74·5	64·4
1 year or more college	18·0	22·4
Median School Years	11·6	12·1
Occupations		
Professional, technical	7·1	10·9
Managers, officers, proprietors	8·1	15·0
Craftsmen (skilled)	21·5	16·5
Operatives (semi-skilled)	21·4	15·7
Clerical, sales	7·2	10·5
Service	4.8	6·2
Labourers (non-farm)	7·5	3·7
Farm labourers	1·4	1·0
Not employed, or active military duty, or not in labour force	20·9	20·5

* Based on a survey of home owners conducted by Bureau of Census for Department of Housing and Urban Development of 2900 mobile homes purchased from 10/1/65 through 9/30/66 and used as primary residences.
† Current population survey.
‡ Totals may not add due to rounding.

Most home owners like the informality and comraderie that goes with a mobile home park. According to recent surveys, the four most important reasons for choosing mobile home living are: (a) less up-keep and maintenance, (b) comfort, (c) lower living costs, and (d) compactness. As for the main disadvantage stated for mobile home living: lack of good parks, it was not related to mobile homes themselves. Some dissatisfaction with the limited amount of living and storage space and with the quality of the mobile homes also turned up. Still 70 per cent of the respondents reported that their next choice in housing would be to buy another mobile home.

5.5. CONCLUSIONS

5.5.1. Future developments

The future of the mobile home industry lies in five areas:

Urban housing. Fixed site town houses, row houses, even high-rise buildings are now being built from mobile units or modules. The greatest untapped potential for the mobile home industry is in its ability to adapt its manufacturing process to the needs of low-cost and moderate priced multi-family housing.

Mobile home communities. These communities utilize the mobile home in its traditional concept. But the needs are changing. New developments must be built in areas of burgeoning population growth; existing ones must be remodelled to keep pace with the increased size of the mobile home and the environmental standards of excellence acceptable to municipalities.

Single site occupancy. About 50 per cent of all mobile homes are currently placed on individually owned property in rural and small town locations. This market is expected to grow with the demand for moderately priced housing and as mobile homes more closely resemble site-built homes in appearance and financing terms.

Vacation or second homes. This market increases with the general economic growth as well as the rise in the segment of the population in the retirement age group.

Fig. 5.10. School-room in double-wide mobile home (from C. R. Sutton: 'Building Homes With Building Blocks'. Steelways, A.I.S.I. Vol. 25, No. 4, Sept.-Oct. 1969).

Commercial and institutional buildings. Fig. 5.10 shows a school room in a double-width mobile home. Banks have used mobile buildings both for temporary and semi-permanent branches.

Barring economic instability and based on a conservative growth forecast of 10 per cent per year, which is considerably less than the growth of the industry experienced in the past, it is estimated that 1974-production could reach 665 000 mobile homes in the three last mentioned areas alone. If the industry succeeds in moving into areas of urban renewal and sectionalized housing in big scale, far greater growth is assured. But housing officials, urban planners and architects who have been waiting to see mobile home companies get into advanced modular housing, have been disappointed up to now. Only 8000 such units were produced in the United States in 1969. The main problem has been to produce a module, particularly for low-cost housing, which would satisfy building codes in various jurisdictions. (In the metropolitan Chicago area alone, there are 47 different codes to contend with). There are signs that this obstacle eventually will be removed. In 1970, California passed a law permitting a factory-built

Fig. 5.11. Apartments in Vicksburg, Miss., build from mobile modules.

house meeting state specifications to be placed anywhere in the state. As part of Operation Breakthrough, the Department of Housing and Urban Development is working for the same to happen on a nation-wide scale. Once the code controversy is solved, introduction on the American market of mass-produced housing modules will un-doubtedly revolutionize building construction practice all over the world. Several of the larger mobile home manufacturers build new plants so that they can easily convert to modules. In the meanwhile, the technical know-how necessary for assembly line production of multi-family housing is building up rapidly.

Fig. 5.11 illustrates what can be done to-day. It is a modular house project which replaced a pocket of negro slum shacks in Vicksburg, Miss. The modules were manufactured within 17 days in a mobile home plant (Magnolia) 10 miles from the city, and carried to the building site by flatbed trucks. The units were hoisted in place by crane. Erection of the units took 8 days. The townhouse units consist of a first floor 12 ft by 32 ft module, containing living-room, kitchen and dining area, storage space and stairwell; a 12 ft by 34 ft second floor with two bedrooms, full bathroom and storage closets. Each two-storey townhouse was produced for $8000 or $10 per square foot, representing a 15–20 per cent savings over comparable conventional construction. Most of the tenants are former residents of the same district. It is a case in point that prohibitions of plastic plumbing by the local building code added $600 per unit in cost. Copper plumbing had to be used.

Other examples of stacked mobile home units are described in some detail in ref (8). But there are others than mobile home companies that try to corner the future market. Materials Systems Corporation, one of the principal award winners in HUD's Operation Breakthrough, build single-family detached dwellings, multi-family apartment buildings up to two stories high, and two storey single-family attached housing, from only five basic types of wall panels, three floor systems and three roof systems. Wall panels are 8 ft high and 20, 40, 70, 100 and 140 in wide. Roof and floor panels are 12×24 ft, 12×36 ft and 12×48 ft. Electric and mechanical systems are attached to, or enclosed in the floor system. The floor panels are built of wood using conventional joist and plywood sheet construction, while sandwich wall and roof panels are made of a blend of glass fibre, polyester resin and inert filler. The panels are factory assembled to form a box and shipped by rail or truck to the construction site. The panels are glued together in the factory. A special glue is applied to all edges where the panels come together at the corners, the floor and ceiling. On contact, a chemical reaction takes place and the panels are fused at their joints.

Looking into the future, there is some speculation on the use of mobile homes as plug-in units in a superstructure or space frame which would act as a high-rise park or a mobile home apartment building.

5.5.2. Summary

Conventional builders all over the world should take a hard look at the building code controversy in the United States, because if the American housing industry manages to break loose, a brand new multibillion dollar industry will be created almost overnight. This may well have the same far reaching effect on the building industry all over the world as the advent of the semiconductor had in the electronic industry, and aircraft had in the transportation field. Builders relying on traditional construction concepts should heed the warning. Radical changes are long overdue in the construction field. Only the mobile home industry has done something radical about it. It developed an entirely new technology, solved the housing problem for millions of American families, cornered a large percentage of the market in 10 years, created quite a few millionaires, and gained a lead over conventional builders for what concerns mass production of to-morrows low-cost modular housing. Finally, it has broken the several thousand year old tradition which tied human dwellings to the land. This will have far reaching technological as well as social and economic consequences.

REFERENCES

1. MOBILE HOME MANUFACTURERS ASSOCIATION (1970). *Flash Facts on Mobile, Sectional and Modular Homes.* (Chicago, Illinois: MHMA).
2. MAYER, L. A. (1970). 'Mobile Homes Move Into the Breach'. *Fortune Magazine,* 127–146.
3. EDWARDS C. M. (1968). 'Dwelling Costs: A Comparison Made of Apartment, Mobile Home, House.' *Mobile Home and Recreational Vehicle Dealer Magazine.* November.
4. ANON. (1968–9). 'Standards for Mobile Homes'. *United States of America Standards Institute.* NFPA No. 501 B, 1968, USA SA 119.1 1969.
5. ROWLAND N. *et al.* (1969). *Reston Low Income Housing Demonstration Program.* Report PB 183 968 (Springfield, Va: Clearinghouse for Federal and Technical Information).
6. ANON. *Woodalls Mobile Home Park Directory.* (Highland Pk., Illinois: Woodall).
7. ANON. (1968). *Housing Survey.* Part 1. *Occupants of New Housing Units.* Part 2. *Mobile Homes and the Housing Supply.* (Washington: U.S. Department of Housing and Urban Development.)
8. ANON. (1970). 'Mobile Way to Meet the Housing Shortage'. *Build International,* p. 261–267.

BIBLIOGRAPHY

BARTLEY E. R., and BAIR F. H. (1960). *Mobile Home Parks and Comprehensive Community Planning.* Studies in Public Administration No. 19. (University of Florida: Public Administration Clearing Service.)
ALPSTEN G. (1970). *Hur mobile homes utvecklades till volymelement.* Byggnadsindustrin, nr. 2.
MOBILE HOME MANUFACTURERS ASSOCIATION. (1970). *Mobile Living. A Complete Guide to Mobile Home Living.* (Chicago, Illinois: MHMA).
HANSEN T. C. (1969). 'Mobile Homes. En revolution inden for amerikansk boligbyggeri'. *Forskning* nr. 10, Kobenhavn.
ANON. (1968). *Mobile Homes and Travel Trailers Industry Report.* Economic Department, Wells Fargo Bank, San Francisco.
DRURY M. J. (1967). *Mobile Homes. The Unrecognized Revolution in American Housing.* (New York State College of Home Economics: Department of Housing and Design).
WEBER H., and BERTHOLD W. (1070). 'Fliessfertigung in der Bauelement Production.' *Industrialisierung des Baues.* Heft 2/3.

6

Reinstatement of fire damaged building structures.

E. Dore, C Eng, M I Struct E, M I C E, M I Mun E
Senior Structural Advisory Engineer of the
Cement and Concrete Association
and
Wm. Sanderson Watts, C Eng, F I C E, F I Struct E, F Weld I,
Consulting Engineer   M Cons E

6.8. A case study on building reinstatement

6.8.1. Description of buildings
6.8.2. Fire
6.8.3. Assessment of damage
6.8.4. Concrete arrangement and programme
6.8.5. Design, drawing, and reconstruction
6.8.6. Finance
6.8.7. Conclusion

Any building which has an inherently fire-protected structural frame of reinforced concrete or concrete-encased structural steel-work should be considered for reinstatement after a fire has taken place, since for such premises it is rarely that complete demolition need occur. Someone with the necessary expertise should therefore specify the repairs which have to be carried out and estimate the cost of reinstatement. This estimate could then be compared with that for demolition and rebuilding.

6.1. ASSESSMENT OF FIRE DAMAGE: PRELIMINARY SURVEY

It is important that the person responsible for specifying fire reinstatement work should be called to survey the fire damage as soon as possible. He will need to collect evidence before the debris is removed. Much background information can be derived from an early inspection which will enable him to build up a picture of the progress, timing, and temperature history of the fire. Apart from this, the client will want his report as quickly as possible in order to brief the demolition workers on the extent of their cleaning-up operations, and to decide whether or not to reinstate with special urgency when consequential losses are running at a high level.

At the conclusion of the fire the local authority surveyor or building inspector will have decided whether or not the structure is in imminent danger of collapse. Nevertheless, the structural engineers' first duty when called to assess a fire-damaged structure is to consider the safety of the structure. Apart from the load-carrying capacity of individual structual members the over-all stability of the building must be considered, since one weak member can, under certain circumstances, affect the safety of the building as a whole. Danger may have arisen as a result of temperature movements, the removal of internal diaphragm walls, or the partial collapse of original strong points. Where scaffolding or shoring is obviously required to ensure the safety of the building it would be as well to specify the position and method in such a way that it would assist in the later repair work as well as in providing temporary security.

Another hazard encountered when entering fire-damaged buildings is the possibility of traps. Unexpected weaknesses may exist in suspended floors where the heat has caused most damage to the soffit, leaving the top surface apparently solid. Infill panels in ribbed floors may be weakened leaving them brittle and liable to sudden collapse under foot traffic or other loading.

When it is considered safe to enter the building or room, all possible clues as to the history of the fire should be carefully recorded before debris is removed. The position and condition of glass, steel, and non-ferrous metals, the melting and charring of any surviving plastics or fabrics can all provide evidence to substantiate an estimate of the time/temperature history of the fire (6).

The detailed examination of the structure should begin with the most conspiciously damaged vertical members including load-bearing walls. This will help to determine whether an adequate load factor exists for the stability of the building in its temporary condition whilst the repairs are carried out. If a fire has taken place in a large building then by charting the degree of fire attack on columns it is possible to plot a pattern of fire intensity across the floor plan of the building. It is desirable, at an early stage of the examination, to attempt to determine such a pattern so that the more detailed examination of columns and beams can be by a sampling technique. Approximate isothermal lines enable the initial evidence to be extrapolated to predict the degree of deterioration throughout the various elements of structure without detailed examination of all parts. Since it is only possible in the early stages to do a limited number of detailed examinations at what are considered to be key points, the isothermal lines can indicate zones for categories of damage requiring different degrees of repair at consequently differing costs.

The preliminary survey, therefore, gathers background information on the fire in order to estimate:

1. The peak temperatures achieved.

2. The duration of peak temperature and rate of build-up and decline of temperature.

3. Evidence of the time during the fire when any significant spalling

of concrete took place. Some evidence may be obtained from the position of spalled fragments relative to other debris. Smoke-covered areas may indicate a more gradual cooling-off rate. Other areas might show considerable heat discoloration without smoke. Clues as to the time of spalling are well worth noting. A broken face left by spalling may show no fire discoloration and is therefore likely to be spalling caused at the end of the fire and associated with a rapid rate of cooling.

4. The extent of any thermal expansion movement of the whole building and its recovery should be determined relative to any possible surrounding datums. These are usually difficult to find but brickwork in staircases or lift shafts provides some evidence. In one fire lack of verticality of the steel lift guide proved a useful indication.

5. Naturally the structural and construction drawings are invaluable at this stage. Anyone who has been engaged in this sort of survey is tempted to declare that it should be standard practice for all such drawings plus copies of calculations to be permanently sealed in a fire-proof compartment for use in cases of emergency.

6. For the reasons mentioned above a close examination of the columns and load-bearing walls to determine the percentage of strength loss as well as the depth of attack must form a part of the pre-liminary survey.

6.2. THE ESSENTIAL EVIDENCE

An assessment must be made of the residual structural capacity of the concrete and steel of which the structural frame is composed. The residual strength of typical structural concretes is indicated in Fig. 6.1. The rate of penetration of heat into concrete members subjected to the standard fire test is indicated in Fig. 6.2. Fortunately, the significant changes in concrete design strength which start to take place normally at 300°C (672°F) are associated with colour changes of the concreting aggregates which are most frequently used (6). Changes of texture and hardness are the superficial signs of temperature effects on concrete which has been significantly heated. The evidence for a reduction in effective structural capacity of concrete can therefore be obtained by visual examination, by judicious use of the Schmidt re-

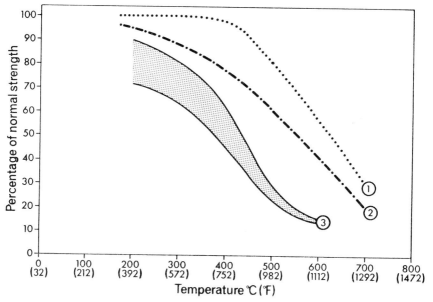

Fig. 6.1. The strength of structural concrete when heated (1 and 2) and the residual strength after cooling (3).

1. Heated concrete strength determined by Furamura (Ref. 4).

2. Heated concrete strength (using 50-mm (2-in) diameter by 101-mm (4-in) long concrete cylinders). Typical curve by Malhotra (Ref. 5).

3. Concrete residual strength on cooling (using 50-mm (2-in) diameter by 101-mm (4-in) long concrete cylinders). This is shown as a zone rather than a line since it covers a range of results (Ref. 5; figs. 7, 9, and 11).

bound hammer and by the careful application of a light hacking tool. The deterioration of a concrete surface is usually far less than the information in Fig. 6.2 would lead us to expect. This is because a normal structural member has sufficient size to be able to replenish the surface with moisture from the interior and draw heat inwards away from the surface attacked by fire.

The residual strength of reinforcement steel after heating is indicated by Fig. 6.3. Both steel reinforcement and structural steel encased in concrete are protected from the spatial temperature of the fire by the concrete around them. In addition steel conducts heat away from the hottest part of the member so that even when the fire tem-

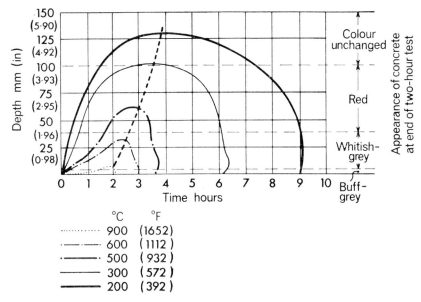

Fig. 6.2a. The penetration of heat into 152-mm (6-in) concrete slab. The standard fire test temperatures were applied to one face for two hours, colour changes were noted. The time taken for temperatures to be reached at each depth can be read from isothermal lines. The internal temperatures lag behind the applied temperatures. The concrete was described as 1:2:4 mix using natural sand and flint gravel (Ref. 6).

peratures exceed 1200°C (2192°F), in a rapid build-up of heat, the steel reinforcement temperature can be kept well below 500°C (932°F) for a considerable period of time. This is vitally important for the stability of the structure at the time of a fire since both the tensile and compressive strengths of steel fall drastically at high fire temperatures (see Fig. 6.4). Provided that there has been no buckling and provided the temperature of the steel has not exceeded 600°C (1112°F) there is unlikely to be any serious reduction in its strength when it has cooled. If there is any possibility that the steel may have reached temperatures in excess of 600°C (1112°F) it would be advisable to take samples of the reinforcement for tensile testing. Such temperatures are rare and are not likely to have been reached unless there is evidence of beam sagging or compression steel buckling. Any

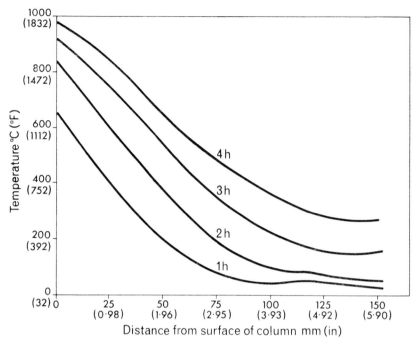

Fig. 6.2b. The temperature gradients in columns, at various times from start of standard fire test in accordance with BS 476 (Ref. 9).

sign of distortion or buckling in reinforcement steel would indicate that replacement or additional steel will be required at these points.

6.3. TESTS TO EVALUATE RESIDUAL STRENGTH

The concrete of the fire-damaged structure can only be sampled by taking the loose lumps which have spalled or were about to spall or by cutting cores. The spalling fragments would be of value as evidence for the preliminary survey as described above. Cores can sometimes be taken from the beams bear their neutral axis at low stress points and occasionally at the top or bottom of rectangular columns. In general, however, unless some members are partially demolished to

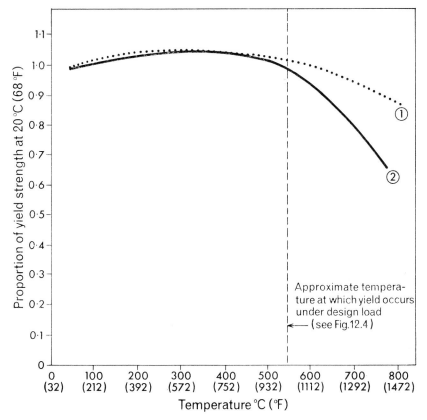

Fig. 6.3. The residual strength of steel reinforcement after heating to various temperatures.
1. HT hot rolled steel to BS 4449.
2. HT cold worked steel to BS 4461 (10).

enable several test cores to be taken from them, it is unlikely that core compression strength tests of any reliable value can be carried out. The information which can, nevertheless, sometimes be obtained from cores is as follows:

(*a*) The quality of the concrete as originally constructed. Control sample cores should be taken whenever possible from parts which have not been fire-damaged.

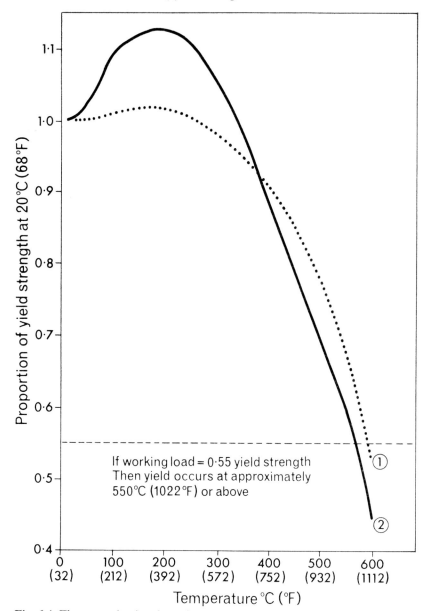

Fig. 6.4. The strength when hot of steel reinforcement heated to various temperatures.

1. HT hot rolled steel to BS 4449.
2. HT cold worked steel to BS 4461 (Ref. 7).

(*b*) Unaffected concrete samples can be subjected to absorption tests, density tests, and chemical analysis tests as a check on the previous strength of the structure and as a basis for comparing with fire-affected concrete.

(*c*) The depth of significant degrees of heat penetration are shown by the colour of layers of the core. This can be used to check the assumptions made by the more superficial method of surface removal in accordance with coloration and texture. Sections of such cores can be compared with cores of the original concrete. The value of this technique has been described by J. K. Green (1).

Where it is necessary to have tensile strength tests on steel reinforcement, as for example on the exposed main steel of suspended floor slabs, it will be necessary to cut a length of 304 mm (12 in) or more, chosen at a point where the curtailed bar can easily be replaced. It is generally noted that down-stand beams and floor soffits suffer spalling equal to, or greater than, columns. The steel, which can be taken from such members more easily than from columns, should indicate a heat of exposure greater than to which the steel in the columns has been exposed.

6.3.1. Calculated residual strength

After the preliminary survey a second, more detailed, survey will be required to plot the detailed evidence not only of columns but also of beams and floor slabs. A schedule for the residual strength of each member of the structure will have to be drawn up so that detailed reinstatement proposals can follow. The residual strength may be shown as a percentage of structural capacity before the fire. Such a previous strength may have been in excess of the original design requirements and also in excess of future service requirements (3). A principle has to be established, therefore, as to whether the building can be reinstated for the net structural requirement of future loading or whether any previous accidental degree of excess capacity (from age factor on concrete and a rounding up of dimensions) has to be preserved. An example of a typical column calculation is given at this stage. Whilst a calculation such as this will relate to a specific member it will act as representative of all the members in the same category. Every detail of the specific member should be given in the calculation to substantiate the value assumed by calculation for its residual strength. As a result of the detailed survey every column, beam, and slab will be placed in a category which indicates that its condition is no worse than that of one of the typical members covered by a detailed calculation. By such examination and calculation the extent of the reinstatement problem can be defined. The techniques to be used for solving the reinstatement problem have then to be chosen. Methods which have been proved to be satisfactory are described below.

6.4. METHODS OF REINSTATEMENT

Where inadequate steel reinforcement remains, and the tensile strength has been seriously reduced, a satisfactory strength replacement will normally only be achieved by increase in the size of the member. It will be cheaper to add additional steel than to attempt to replace what is already in position. Additional main steel will require additional secondary steel and also new fire protection concrete around it. The thickness of the new concrete cover may possibly be reduced if a vermiculite plaster rendering is also applied. In the majority of cases, however, the original steel will not be adversely affected and all that will be required is replacement cover concrete of adequate quality.

Where the steel reinforcement is still adequate the operation of replacing concrete usually falls into one of the following categories:

6.4.1. Isolated small patches

This is usually quite rare since spalling normally indicates that a wider zone than that which has actually spalled away has been affected to some degree. Where, however, a short length of no more than 200 mm (7·9 in) has spalled (perhaps because of a very real local weakness) leaving absolutely sound concrete around, a plastering technique may be used to patch up such relatively superficial damage. For such small patches a PVA bonding agent may be added to the gauging water to improve adhesion or, alternatively, epoxy resin mortar may be used.

6.4.2. Larger areas of shallow deterioration

When the full depth of unsound concrete has been removed by a light electric or pneumatic tool, leaving a roughened yet sound surface free from grease or soot, a light steel fabric (weight approximately 1·5 kg/m³–2·7 lb/yd²) should be positioned by shot-fired nails against the exposed concrete face but separated from it by a gap of 12 mm (0·47 in). Gunite concrete can then be applied in thin layers against the original concrete and around the additional mesh reinforcement. The Gunite concrete suitable for most applications will have a minimum equivalent works cube strength of 21 N/mm² (3000 lbf/in²). (This might be difficult to guarantee where Gunite has to be placed behind reinforcement of 16 mm (0·62 in) diameter and over.) This method of replacing the concrete cover is often preferred since it can be applied to horizontal, vertical, and sloping surfaces (2). It can be used for building up substantial thicknesses, although considerable care has to be taken in dealing with corners and reveals where a percentage of sand may rebound and be trapped to form pockets of weakness. Normally a space of 35 mm (1·37 in) behind main reinforcing bars or 12 mm (0·47 in) behind mesh reinforcement is necessary before concrete can be reliably placed by the Guniting method.

6.5. INCREASING MEMBER SIZES

When thicknesses of 50 mm (2 in) and more have to be added to columns, which will always be the case when additional main reinforcing steel is required, casting within shutters is a practical method. It will be necessary to apply a degree of vibration to the formwork. Except in the case of very narrow beams it is impossible to use this method for placing and considering the concrete at the centre of the underside of a beam. If the tops of beams at floor level require replacement concrete, there are no such practical difficulties. In the tops of beams the water/cement ratio may be reduced to approximately 0·4 on the understanding that the optimum amount of compaction will be achieved by careful placing and punning by electric or pneumatic tools. A water-reducing admixture should be used for replacement concrete. This ensures that sufficient workability can be obtained whilst water/cement ratios are kept in all cases below 0·55.

These techniques result in the replacement of concrete which will be structurally and fire-protectively effective because it will be intimately tied to the original concrete by links, stirrups, or additional mesh reinforcement.

6.5.1. Repairs to columns

Any column which is reduced to less than three-quarters of its original design strength (not three-quarters of its strength immediately before the fire) is likely to have been relieved of part of the dead loading by emergency propping. Care will have been taken to ensure that such temporary works transmit the load all the way down to the foundations or spread it in such a way as not to create dangerous local shear conditions in the beams of lower floors. After such temporary propping, all the concrete which has deteriorated or is known to have reached temperatures in excess of 300°C (572°F) can be removed. This work should be done by workmen instructed to detect by colour and hardness indications the extent of removal that is necessary. The conscientious workman soon begins to appreciate the hardness of sound concrete! The less-conscientious workman may be inclined not to cut far enough and the supervisor's hammer and chisel should be used in the final inspection before reinstatement concrete is placed. The main steel reinforcement may be partially or completely exposed by this work. Even when additional main reinforcement is not required it is sometimes advisable to supply additional links around the existing bars, since the existing links may have been disturbed, or perhaps the links provided in the original construction would not be considered adequate in the light of more recent design requirements. The nominal requirement for links contained in the present design code (12) is barely adequate for columns with high steel percentages requiring 2 hours, fire-resistance. In severe fire cases it has been found that local weaknesses in link anchorages have resulted in buckling of longitudinal reinforcement. If individual links have to be removed the main longitudinal steel can be temporarily supported by steel bands of the type used in packaging (as, for example, by reinforcement suppliers for bundles of bars and by brick manufacturers for palette loads of bricks). In a case where the reinstatement does not call for additional longitudinal steel the replacement concrete will provide protection against any future fires. A replacement concrete or Gunite layer of 50 mm (2 in) thickness placed around a central layer of fabric reinforcement provides a heat shield of considerably increased durability compared with an original column with minimum links.

A safe assumption which is sometimes made is that the new concrete does not absorb any of the dead load when it is reapplied because of the shrinkage of the new material. Strain in the old material, however, is sufficient to cause a redistribution of load into the new concrete cover when superimposed loadings occur. The validity of such an arbitrary assumption must be reassessed in the case of each structure where it is intended that the new material should be load-bearing.

In the majority of cases where columns have lost as much as 25 per cent of their original design strength it will usually be necessary to supply additional main reinforcing bars. These bars will require links in accordance with the code of practice rules for design. Fabric should also be provided in the thickness of the new cover concrete if it exceeds 40 mm (1·5 in) thickness. This, in turn, will depend upon the fire-resistance of the column. The extra concrete provided will be stressed, when the column is again loaded, in three ways. Firstly, despite the shrinkage of the new concrete, axial longitudinal compression can be effectively dispersed from the core concrete into the new concrete across the interface. Secondly, as soon as the original column core is restressed the new concrete is subjected to the bursting forces resulting from the Poisson's Ratio expansion of the core concrete normal to the plane of its axial loading. Steel links in the new concrete make it possible for this new outer skin to induce triaxial compression in the more highly loaded original column core. Thirdly, the new concrete absorbs stress as a result of creep strain in the core concrete. When this occurs the additional loading which is applied to the column produces axial stresses which are more uniformly distributed over the width of the column, including the new concrete.

Any column which is found to have a sloping diagonal crack passing entirely through it will require special treatment. This is a feature which might result from considerable relative horizontal movement of the floors at the top and bottom of the column. In such a case the column will have been replaced by props at an early stage and the whole of the original concrete section can be removed at the effected level. Sometimes the main steel reinforcement may be kept in position provided that it is not buckled. If it is buckled, additional steel, well lapped, will be required to replace it.

6.5.2. Repairs to beams

The deterioration of the concrete is generally greatest in the bottom zone of the beam. Here the replacement of cover concrete, either with or without the addition of extra tensile reinforcement, will be by Guniting, plastering, or casting in shutters as described above. Great care is required in specifying the repairs to areas of beams which have been subjected to cracking, especially those beams which have cracked in the compression zone at the ends of beams. Vertical and diagonal cracks may have been opened up as a result of the resistance of the columns to the expansion and contraction of the beams during the fire and subsequent cooling. Full depth sections of cracked but otherwise sound concrete may have to be broken out and recast, but only if the cracks leave an insufficient shear capacity in the beam. In such a case part of the floor above the beam might have to be cut out to make this repair practicable. The repair of major cracks of this type is very rarely required. Fine cracks in the end zones of continuous beams or beams with a reasonable quantity of continuity steel and shear stirrups will have little effect on the shear capacity of the beam. One result of such cracks could be some additional rotation at the ends and a redistribution of bending moment to increase the positive moment at the centre of the beam. A reasonable assumption regarding this redistribution might lead to the decision to increase the amount of bottom steel at the middle of the span when the reinstatement operation is carried out at that point. A fine vertical crack measuring less than 0·1 mm (0·004 in) wide in the shear zone of the beam can therefore be ignored if the beam is provided with adequate shear reinforcement and top tensile reinforcement for negative moment resistance.

When beams have to be made larger at midspan it is frequently more acceptable to widen downstand beams than to make them deeper, although from the design point of view this is perhaps less effective. If it were possible to deepen the beam the new reinforcement could be made to accept its tensile load immediately whereas when new reinforcement is placed at the same level as the existing reinforcement, the new steel could only become loaded by redistribution of load from the existing steel. The comments made above with regard to links in columns apply equally to stirrups in beams. Stirrups contribute considerably to the ultimate load capacity of the structure in fire conditions. Three methods have been employed for fixing stirrups into position. They are:

(*a*) By drilling horizontally well into sound concrete at the top of the beam and using patent types of expanding bolt.

(*b*) By completing the formation of the full stirrup passing through prepared holes in the floor above produced by diamond core drills or thermic lance.

(*c*) By welding new stirrups to the exposed existing ones.

6.5.3. Repairs to floors

The lighter forms of ribbed floors and composite floors using precast units frequently have to be completely replaced. In such cases the fire deterioration is so bad that they are not difficult to demolish. Solid concrete slab floors are more likely to be reinstated by the Guniting technique. In the majority of cases the steel reinforcement, even when exposed, has been little affected by the fire. The concrete cover may have spalled or been damaged but still have achieved its protection role. It is then necessary to cut back the remaining patches of unsound concrete to above the exposed reinforcement, so providing a sound interface for the Gunite concrete replacement. Additional reinforcement in the form of separate bars or additional structural fabric can be fixed if necessary to any layer of existing reinforcement which itself may be inadequate but remains thoroughly bonded. Guniting concrete cover to the soffits of floors has been found to be effective and reliable provided preparation has been adequate and the work carried out by skilled workmen.

6.6. SATISFACTORINESS OF REINSTATEMENT METHODS

In some instances the repaired building has lost a minimal amount of floor space or head-room as a result of an increase in column or beam dimensions. For such a small disadvantage it is possible to restore a building to its original strength and in most instances to increase appreciably its resistance to further fire hazards. Recent research has emphasized the considerable contribution made by mesh reinforcement in the cover zones of concrete members. The new replacement or extra concrete will have been placed with meticulous care and will be a more reliable product as a result. Above all, the reinstatement of a fire-damaged building has been shown in several notable instances to have been far quicker and much less expensive than its complete demolition and rebuilding. Similar methods to those described above have been used for the reinstatement of a multistorey factory, and of a large department store in Lincoln (11). Both are examples of reinstatement after fires not likely to be exceeded in severity for those types of building.

One of the important cost elements in evaluating reconstruction proposals is the time taken for the building to be replaced and to become operational again. It is estimated by the Co-operative Society, whose department store was reinstated at Lincoln, that a complete rebuilding operation would have taken twelve months longer than the time which was actually taken for its reinstatement. Because of the way in which the site was wedged between two roads and adjacent properties it was without adequate working space for a complete demolition and reconstruction. The disturbance to the general public, to road traffic, and to other businesses adjacent, was kept to a minimum. Naturally the reinstatement operation involved some noise, dust, and disturbance but this was largely contained within the confines of the building by the remaining shell.

In that operation 4064 tonnes (4000 tons) of concrete were removed and replaced and 152 tonnes (150 tons) of new reinforcing steel were installed. In many cases demolition takes place without a proper evaluation of alternatives. In this case, however, the building owner obtained a rapid and realistic engineering appraisal from structural engineers and builders working together.

Industrial structures are more prone to fire damage than others, and frequently the damage is restricted to areas adjacent to combustible storage. Reinstatement of parts of frames is extremely common, but a recent case following a severe fire in part of a ten storey factory in Hong Kong is notable. Although the fire was restricted to one-quarter of the fifth floor, it burnt for about eight hours. That floor was used as a button factory and the fire load consisted mainly of plastics. Despite severe damage to columns the reinstatement was carried out whilst normal work continued on the upper floors. Because of the column distortion resulting from the differential movement of upper and lower floors many of the columns on the fifth floor were completely re-placed. Exposure to severe fire is an unwelcome occurrence for any structure. If it survives in a state which is capable of economic re-instatement the careful and painstaking repairs involved can result in a structure equal to the original in strength and with a greater resistance to any subsequent fire.

6.7. TYPICAL COLUMN REINSTATEMENT CALCULATION

Example of a calculation to compare the strength of an original column with the strength of a reinstated column of the same size.

In this calculation the strength of steel is not taken into account. If the residual steel strength is less than 100 per cent then some additional steel can be added. New links and wrapping mesh can be added as required.

This calculation follows the pattern of a suggested calculation contained in reference (8).

Condition before the fire

Original concrete section area (ignoring steel)
$$= 450 \times 300 = 135\,000 \text{ mm}^2$$
If this had been designed using a two-month age factor (CP 114 Table 9) the equivalent area of concrete
$$= 1 \cdot 1 \times 135\,000 = 148\,500 \text{ mm}^2$$

Condition after fire

1. Assume that heat to the extent of 400°C (752°F) and above had penetrated to a depth of 45 mm (1·8 in) and destroyed the structural effectiveness of the concrete to that depth. (Actual contours of this will be determined by detailed inspection.)

2. Assume that the core at a temperature not exceeding 200°C (392°F) has not lost strength.

3. Assume that the layer between (1) and (2) was 30 mm (1·2 in) and remained sound but had lost an average of 75 per cent of its compressive strength.

Proposed column reinstatement

The column would consist of equivalent areas as follows:

1. Original core (assumed size)
   $300 \times 150 \times 1\cdot24$ (age factor) $= 55\ 800\ \text{mm}^2$

2. Intermediate zone (as idealized)
   $2 \times 30\ (330 + 180) \times 0\cdot75$ (deterioration factor) $= 22\ 950\ \text{mm}^2$

3. Replacement concrete (nominal 3500 lbf/in²)
   at 28 days say

   $2 \times 45\ (405 + 255) \times \dfrac{3\cdot5}{3\cdot0} \times 1\cdot1$ (age factor 2 months)

                                                   $= 76\ 239\ \text{mm}^2$

                                      Total Area $154\ 980\ \text{mm}^2$

By this calculation the reinstated strength will exceed the original design strength (154 980 compared with 148 500). If the full strength of the column before the fire had to be replaced, then the equivalent new concrete area would need to have been equal to $135\ 000 \times 1\cdot24 = 167\ 400\ \text{mm}^2$. To increase the equivalent area to that value the above calculation suggests that either additional steel reinforcement would be required or the concrete section would have to be enlarged or the replacement concrete strength would have to be increased. All three methods are appropriate and any or all of them may be used to produce a column of the required strength.

6.8. A CASE STUDY ON BUILDING REINSTATEMENT

The project described arose as the result of a fire which occurred in the multistorey concrete-framed buildings of a large food production plant. Engineering involvement was necessary during the period of the actual fire, subsequently in the assessment of damage, and throughout the design and construction techniques for remedial works. At all times the solutions chosen and their methods of execution, whilst respecting finance, had to be such that the over-all objective of reinstating full production facilities within the minimum period of time could be achieved with the minimum interruption of food production.

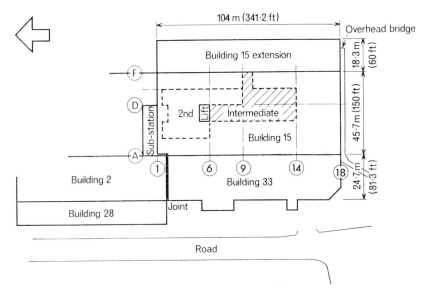

Fig. 6.5. Layout and identification of case study buildings.

6.8.1. Description of buildings

The building complex in which the fire occurred comprised an area of approximately 183 × 91 m (600 × 300 ft). Progressive development had taken place over a number of years and identification of the particular buildings can be appreciated from Fig. 6.5. During development the only expansion joint incorporated was that running east–west on Line 1.

Building 2 and Building 15 were designed by American consultants and it was found that on certain aspects American practice had been adopted. The remainder of the buildings were carried out by British consultants to CP 114.

The buildings to the west of Line A, Fig. 6.5, are approximately 24 m (80 ft) wide and have five floors plus a basement. Building 15 and the extension east of Line F have fewer floors and no basement.

As part of the phased development the initial construction south of Line 1 comprised Building 15 only and the columns on A and F lines were pocketed on the west and east face respectively to receive beams when the development of Building 15 extension and Building 33 proceeded.

Fig. 6.6. Removal of fire-damaged materials.

The columns, on a basic 9 × 6 m (30 × 20 ft) grid, were generally 965 × 559 mm (38 × 22 in) on A and F lines with internal columns being up to 609 mm (24 in) square. Beams were in the order of 863 and 914 mm (34 and 36 in) deep over-all with widths varying between 381 and 457 mm (15 and 18 in). Imposed loading, which was fully utilized, was 1220·6 kgf/m² (250 lbf/ft²) and all columns were founded on reinforced concrete piles.

6.8.2. Fire

The fire was observed initially at the centre of the plant adjacent to the lift shaft on Line 6. Quantities of flammable materials were stored on the first floor (British ground floor) in heights up to 3·5 m (11·5 ft).

The fire spread rapidly and for a period smoke and heat made the entire building untenable. At first it was possible to fight the fire from the exterior only and 47 appliances and 350 firemen were in attendance.

It was decided that the only satisfactory means of rapidly and completely beating a fire involving such large amounts of burning and smouldering material was to remove such materials and Fig. 6.6

Fig. 6.7. Fire damage to structure.

shows one of the caterpillar-tracked machines which was used to transfer the debris into metal bodied lorries. Whilst this operation was carried out water hoses were played continually on to the materials and vehicles. After the fire had been brought under control, engineering opinion was requested with regard to the condition and likely behaviour of the structure. Fig. 6.7 and 6.8 illustrate conditions when the fire had been brought under control but not completely extinguished.

6.8.3. Assessment of damage

As stated, the overriding demand was the re-establishment of production facilities, although not at unlimited cost, hence engineering

Fig. 6.8. Fire damage to structure.

judgement had to be adopted at the expense of any prolonged investigational techniques and test methods, however desirable.

At the time literature and information relating to the repair of fire-damaged buildings appeared to be lacking and, even where available, was devoid of detail. The following items define general factors relating to the influence of fire on concrete buildings and they formed the basis on which many decisions were taken:

(*a*) Fire is accidental overload.

(*b*) Unequal effects of heat load cause deformation in the structure as a whole and in part.

(*c*) The coefficient of thermal expansion is not the same at all temperatures and is higher than that of contraction for concrete heated to temperatures in the order of 535°C (995°F).

(*d*) Aggregates have a great influence on the fire-resistance of construction, the type of aggregate affects thermal conductivity, diffusivity, and the coefficient of expansion of the concrete.

(*e*) The greatest disadvantage of concrete elements in a fire is spall-

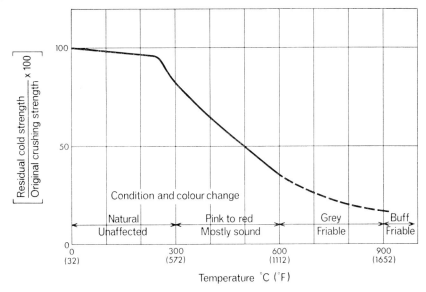

Fig. 6.9. The effect of heat on concrete.

ing. Explosive spalling results in the removal of successive layers, while 'sloughing' off occurs chiefly in beams and columns, i.e. cracks form parallel to the arrises and concrete becomes detached to a depth of some plane of weakness such as reinforcement.

Colour change of concrete serves as a basic indicator and Fig. 6.9 gives general guidance on colour change/temperature/strength relationship. The following temperature criteria are worthy of noting when considering fire-damaged concrete:

(*a*) Colour-change.

(*b*) Surface cracking approximately 285°C (545°F).

(*c*) Deeper cracking approximately 535°C (995°F).

(*d*) Spalling over reinforcement steel to expose part of the bar 790°C (1454°F).

(*e*) In the absence of tests, pink concrete and beyond can be considered to demand respect.

For the project described the general fire temperature was estimated as 750–850°C (1382–1562°F) and samples of the concrete from failed

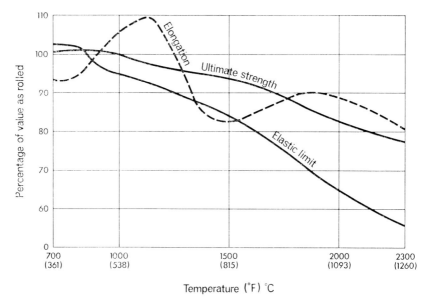

Temperature (°F) °C

Fig. 6.10. The effect of heat on reinforcement.

beams showed a colour change to buff indicating a temperature in the region of 850–900°C (1562–1652°F).

Concrete in general has a lower strength after cooling from a given temperature than when at that temperature and is also influenced by load.

Inward progression of temperature rise within a member is influenced by:

(*a*) Duration and intensity of the fire.

(*b*) Extent of spalling.

(*c*) Thermal diffusivity and conductivity of the concrete.

(*d*) Extra insulating value of dehydrated concrete.

(*e*) Shape, thickness, and any loss of cross-section.

Steel reinforcement in the beams and columns was generally mild steel and the fire treatment received must have resulted in a mixture of annealing/normalizing/hardening/tempering. Fig. 6.10 gives some indication of heat effects on such reinforcement, showing:

(*a*) Slight increase in elastic limit over the value as rolled up to a temperature of about 425°C (797°F) then a gradual decrease as the temperature increases.

(*b*) Ultimate strength shows a slight gain up to a temperature of 480–535°C (896–995°F) and drops similarly but at a slower rate than the elastic limit.

(*c*) Percentage elongation decreases until temperatures between 370 and 427°C (700 and 800°F) are reached, then increases rapidly to a temperature of 600°C (1110°F) as the rolled stresses are relieved then decreases about as rapidly until a temperature of 815°C (1500°F) is obtained. After this a slight increase takes place up to 1038°C (1900°F) and finally a decrease as grain growth begins.

The foregoing with respect to steel and concrete is merely a guide for making judgement and it has to be acknowledged that the surface of the concrete may have been roasted and then given shock treatment by a deluge of cold water.

For the buildings concerned an early assessment was made of damage, design requirements, reconstruction programme, and estimated cost of remedial works. The work was basically divided into three parts:

(*a*) Safety, temporary shoring, and initial demolition.

(*b*) Remedial works to Building 33.

(*c*) Remedial works to Building 15.

Primary damage, Fig. 6.11 was obvious and the initial demolition requirements were easily defined.

An assessment of the extent of secondary damage also required early attention to decide if a temporary reduction was necessary for imposed loading and whether any production plant had to be relocated to permit remedial work to proceed.

With superficial removal of debris an inspection was made of the concrete and exposed reinforcement, notes were made of surface crazing, deeper cracks together with extent and depth of spalling, colour of concrete, degree of exposure, and apparent condition of steel. Samples were cut from both the concrete and steel and tested to assist in deciding between demolition and remedial work.

Beams which had stirrups behaved in a most commendable manner but beams devoid of stirrups suffered badly, cover spalling off permitting the heat to get at the main reinforcement which unfortunately was not adequately tied.

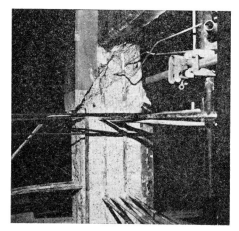

Fig. 6.11. Primary damage to
9 m (30 ft) beam.
Fig. 6.12. Fire damage 9 × 6 m
(30 × 20 ft) beam and
slab soffit.
Fig. 6.13. Major fracture to
columns on Line **D**.

Fig. 6.12 shows the effect of fire damage to the soffit of the slabs and to a 9 m (30 ft) span beam which had been constructed without even nominal links throughout its length. Generally the 6 m (20 ft) span girder beams had, due to shear requirements, steel links and the effect of such links holding the concrete cover in place can be appreciated from this illustration.

It was found that secondary reinforcing steel in the form of links was an important factor in retaining concrete which had been subjected to fire damage. The Fire Research Station have recently completed a research programme which should provide information on the effectiveness of methods of retaining concrete cover in position.

It was noted that the most severely damaged columns were not those that endured the direct heat at the heart of the fire but those which received horizontal forces from beams due to thermal expansion and contraction.

Damage on Line D between Grid 6 and 9 (Fig. 6.5) was particularly severe. Three columns on Line D were found to be sheared completely on a 45° plane with the longitudinal reinforcement badly deformed. Fig. 6.13 shows the condition of these columns after partial demolition of adjacent floor areas.

A crack occurred at all floor levels in Building 33 where it adjoined Building 15 on Line A. The crack occurred for the full length of the building and, due to thermal movement, fracture and spalling also took place at all the pocket seatings provided in the original columns.

Production facilities were maintained wherever possible and reinforced concrete platforms located in fire-damaged areas, but themselves undamaged, were suspended from upper floors which had been unaffected by the fire.

6.8.4. Concrete arrangement and programme

The project, involving assessment of damage, design, drawing, contract negotiation and control, together with site supervision, was undertaken by a team resident on site where all design and drawing work was carried out and from where all day-to-day direction of the project took place.

The construction contract was on a negotiated basis, from a selected short list of contractors, comprising a percentage fee form of prime cost contract supported by a specification and supplementary schedules for tools, plant, and labour.

The general contractor provided layout and material for all restoration work except power services and decoration, which were the subject of separate contracts due to these being closely related to the reinstatement of production equipment.

The conditions of contract basically described requirements as:

(*a*) Propping as required.

(*b*) Cutting away to ascertain damage.

(*c*) Demolition.

(*d*) Reconstruction of badly damaged aspects.

(*e*) Remedial works to other damaged aspects.

Over-all reconstruction proposals were programmed initially on a bar line basis. A planning engineer was engaged on site to prepare a critical path analysis and to keep this under continual review. Amendments were made as necessary to take into account additional work, changes in sequence to suit production requirements, and labour availability.

Weekly site meetings were held with minutes issued within twenty-four hours. Contract documentation, negotiation, and design work were advanced at a rate which permitted initial remedial work in reconstruction on Line A, at the junction between Building 15 and 33, to commence within four days of the start of the fire and general reconstruction was well advanced within three weeks.

6.8.5. Design, drawing, and reconstruction

The general factors determining areas to be removed were as follows:

(*a*) Temperature and duration of fire, reducing the strength of concrete and properties of steel below safe values.

(*b*) Depth of spalling.

(*c*) Shear cracks.

(*d*) General location with reference to satisfactory construction joints.

(*e*) Relative cost of methods of repair.

Three methods for restoration were considered:

(*a*) Complete replacement, which involved the problem of taking care of shrinkage at joints in floors and columns where the area being replaced was completely surrounded by old sections.

(*b*) The addition of fire-proofed structural steel, which lead to large members and, sometimes, difficult connections.

(*c*) Gunite repair, with a problem of screening and protection together with matching of finishes.

When executing the work the following facts were kept in mind:

(*a*) Deteriorated concrete was to be removed. This included spalled, friable, cracked, and porous-looking concrete, bearing in mind the use of colour as a guide.

(*b*) Chipping was to be carried out to a depth where real resistance was met. This was found most effectively by striking the concrete with a handpick, particularly when preparing surfaces for Gunite.

Fig. 6.14. Reinstatement of beams and slab at second floor.

(*c*) No more concrete than necessary must be cut away from round the main reinforcement.

Demolition started at the second floor, working on an area that was to be entirely opened up, this being advantageous in view of the fact that the building was still contracting and cooling.

Within three weeks of the fire, reinforcement was being fixed at second-floor level, Fig. 6.14, information being issued to the contractor in two stages, formwork profiles followed by reinforcement details.

During demolition and reconstruction of the floor beams, production facilities were maintained if possible in adjacent bays, and design consideration was given to maintaining continuity of beams or to establishing the effect of lack of continuity.

Remedial works to beams involved either:

(*a*) Complete reconstruction.

(*b*) Supplementary steel lattice girders with Gunite.

Fig. 6.15. Reinstated beams using lattice girders and Gunite.

(*c*) Supplementary steel stirrups with Gunite.
(*d*) Mesh reinforcement with Gunite.
Where lattice girders were used at each side of an existing concrete beam they provided all necessary structural support to the slab above, the slab achieving bearing on the flange of the top boom angles to the girders. The existing concrete beams were left in position and supported between the steel lattice girders, the latter being wrapped in mesh and Gunite applied to give a finished appearance as shown in Fig. 6.15.

A works office area located over the intermediate floor was quickly restored for occupation, this being propped from first-floor level. Props were arranged to permit the construction of new floor beams.

As previously stated the columns suffered varying degrees of damage, and remedial work to columns was dealt with under three headings:

Fig. 6.16. Temporary steel towers for column replacement, Line D.

(*a*) Replacement of intermediate lengths.

(*b*) Encasement by adding a further skin, so increasing plan area and stiffness.

(*c*) Jacketing, similar to encasement but penetrated by existing beams.

Carrying out the replacement of intermediate lengths to columns on Line D involved the supply and erection of steel towers, Fig. 6.16, each supporting over 406 tonnes (400 tons). Completed columns, beams, and slabs carried out by this method are shown in Fig. 6.18.

Many columns suffered damage which could be made good by either Gunite or concrete encasement. In a number of columns between second- and third-floor levels the fracture planes were multiple and in all directions, although there was no deformation and no

Fig. 6.17. Jacketing to fractured columns.

deterioration of material due to heat. These columns were repaired by binding with welded steel rings and concrete encasing.

Virtually all the columns on Line F and a number on Line A had reinforced concrete jacketing applied. This system was decided upon after detailed design analysis, otherwise reconstruction would have been necessary similar to the columns on Line D which would have involved considerable interruption of production, excessive propping and screening, and a severe prolongation of construction. Fig. 6.17

Fig. 6.18. Reinstated beams and columns.

illustrates the restricted conditions under which the jacketing was carried out.

6.8.6. Finance

Financial control of the project was directed and progressed through the weekly meetings and by the employment of a resident quantity surveyor on site. In conjunction with the contractors' surveyor he was responsible for the preparation and submission to the engineer of monthly certificates of payment.

Monthly estimates of final cost were prepared based on up-to-date work appreciation and experience gained during running of the project, the results being submitted to the client and insurers with detailed comparison against the initial estimate.

6.8.7. Conclusion

The first reaction upon surveying a smoke-blackened scene, with damage as described above, tends to be that, surely, nothing could be saved. However, it has been shown that much can be saved and much of the damage repaired.

This particular building had hardly been restored to the condition shown in Fig. 6.18, when paper storage was once again to maximum height, but this time with a sprinkler system installed!

REFERENCES

1. GREEN, J. K. (1971). 'Reinstatement of concrete structures after fire', *Architects' Journal* (14 and 21 July), p. 93–99, 151–5 (also C & CA reprint 94 007).
2. —— and LONG, W. B. (1971). 'Gunite repairs to fire damaged concrete structures', *Concrete* Vol. 5, No. 4, p. 118–22.
3. MALHOTRA, H. L. (1969). 'Fire Resistance of Structural Concrete Beams', *Fire Research Note no. 741* (Fire Research Station).
4. BALDWIN, R., and NORTH, M. A. (1969). 'Stress-Strain Curves of Concrete at High Temperatures', *Fire Research Note no. 785* (Fire Research Station).
5. MALHOTRA, H. L. (1956). 'The effect of temperature on the compressive strength of concrete', *magazine of Concrete Research* Vol. 8, No. 23, p. 85–94.
6. PARKER, T. W., and NURSE, R. W. (1950) (Part I); BERSEY, G. E. (1950) (Part II). 'Investigation on Building Fires: Part I—Estimation of Maximum Temperatures; Part II—Colour Changes in Concrete', *National Building Studies Technical Paper*, no. 4 (London: HMSO).
7. BANNISTER, J. L. (1971). 'Steel reinforcement and tendons for structural concrete', *The Consulting Engineer* Vol. 35, No. 2, pp. 80–99.
8. ANON. (1946). 'Reinforced concrete columns damaged by fire', 'Repair of Damaged Buildings', *Building Research Note* no. 18.
9. THOMAS, F. G., and WEBSTER, C. T. (1953). Investigation on Building Fires: Part VI—The Fire Resistance of Reinforced Concrete Columns', *National Building Studies Research Paper* no. 18 (London: HMSO).
10. STEVENS, R. F. (1966). Contribution to a discussion on a paper by R. I. Lancaster, 'Steel reinforcement', *Structural Concrete* Vol. 3, No. 4.
11. ANON. 'The reinstatement of Co-operative House', The Simons Construction Group Ltd (Lincoln) (private document).
12. BRITISH STANDARDS INSTITUTION (1969). *The Structural Use of Reinforced Concrete in Buildings*, CP 114: Part 2 (London: BSI).

7

Computer aided luminance design of interiors

John W. Simpson, B Sc, M Sc, M Inst P
and
David Carter, B Sc, MSc
Department of Building,
University of Manchester Institute of Science and Technology

7.1. Introduction

7.2. The design method
　　7.2.1. The roles of designer and computer
　　7.2.2. Restrictions placed on the method
　　7.2.3. Stages in the program suite

7.3. Program application
　　7.3.1. Design for an office
　　7.3.2. Exploration of alternative solutions

7.4. Conclusions

7.1. INTRODUCTION

In designing the artificial lighting installation for an interior, lighting engineers and designers usually make use of the conventional lumen design method (1) coupled with a glare index calculation (2).

The lumen method takes as its starting point a given type of luminaire and a required working surface illuminance. This method does not yield information about the lighting of the other surfaces such as the walls or ceiling. If the design of the visual environment is to be meaningful, then consideration must extend beyond simply providing sufficient illuminance on the visual task.

A number of methods of lighting design which take into account the total appearance of the installation have been put forward. For example, the method due to Waldram (3) is based on the concept of apparent brightness and that of Hopkinson (4) on the idea of luminance ratios. In such cases, the initial specification for the room includes either the luminances of all the major surfaces in the room, or the apparent brightness from which the luminances can be derived if the adaptation level is known. The ensuing calculations determine the distributions of the reflected and direct flux on the walls, ceiling and working plane and lead to the choice of a luminaire which will give the desired total appearance to the room.

The total appearance or luminance design method provides much more useful information than the lumen method and also provides a more satisfactory basis for the choice of the luminaire. Unfortunately the luminance design methods contain tedious calculations and they are unlikely to be undertaken as a routine operation by the lighting designer except perhaps for prestige jobs.

This article describes a suite of computer programmes which has been written to assist the designer in using the luminance design method. The basis for the programs is derived from the manual calculation methods described by Coomber and Jay in the IES monograph No. 10 (5).

The design of the general lighting of an office will be used to illustrate the ways in which the programs could be employed in the design sequence.

7.2. THE DESIGN METHOD

7.2.1. The roles of designer and computer

The suite of programs has been developed in three stages and the overall pattern of the design method and the relationship of the stages are shown in Fig. 7.1.

It will be noted that the designer and computer have been each assigned definite roles. The choice of a suitable specification of luminances and reflectances, and the selection and layout of luminaries are within the province of the designer whereas the computer will perform set algorithms for the arithmetical calculations to provide information to help the designer in decision making. The computer when used in an on-line conversational mode will function as an immediate design aid.

The program suite which is written in TELCOMP 2 language has been developed using a commercially available on-line time sharing system. Access to the central computer is obtained through a remote teleprinter terminal which is connected to the central processor by GPO telephone lines. Input may be by punched paper tape and tape reader or manually via the keyboard of the teleprinter. Output is by typed statements and results on the paper roll of the teleprinter.

In operation, the three program stages are filed in the computer store and on the command of the designer these may become readily available for computations. The various stages may be initiated by the designer using a simple instruction such as:

DO PART 1

and thereafter the computer provides the cues requesting information from the designer. For example, the teleprinter prints:

LENGTH

to which the designer must respond with the value of the length of the room using an appropriate format. The record would then show:

LENGTH 12.000

The program then progresses by either cueing further responses or by providing computed results.

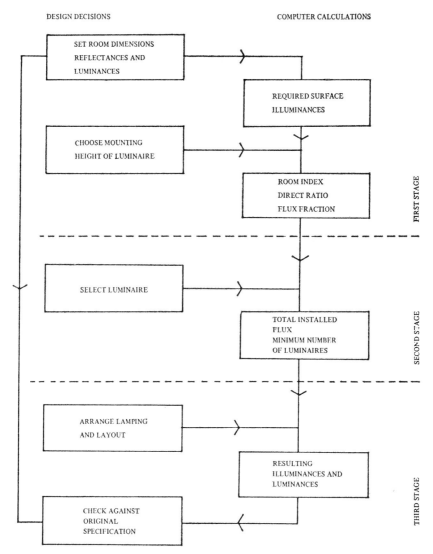

Fig. 7.1. Luminance design method. The roles of the designer and the computer.

7.2.2. Restrictions placed on the method

The suite of programs is applicable to rooms in the form of rectangular prisms and bounded by surfaces which approximate to diffusing reflectors. It is assumed that the proposed artificial lighting installation will consist of a conventional array of regularly spaced luminaries: the programs do not make allowances for any natural light provided by windows or roof lights.

Values for illuminance and luminance have been averaged over the full area of each wall, working plane or ceiling surface. In its present form, the program suite cannot deal with surfaces sub-divided into zones with different luminances.

To simplify the inter-reflection calculations Hisano's (6) approximation for equivalent square rooms has been used. This places a restriction on the room dimensions to the effect that the ratio of length to width must not be greater than 4 and the room index not less than 0·25.

7.2.3. Stages in the program suite

Using the desired luminances and reflectances of the walls, ceiling and working plane or floor as a starting point, *the first stage program* computes the total, indirect and direct illuminances which will be required on each of the surfaces if the desired luminance pattern is to be achieved. The designer must now specify the mounting height of the luminaire and the program will yield the direct ratio, ceiling ratio and flux fraction for an appropriate installation. This information may be simply translated into a luminaire specification of British zonal classification (BZ), upward and downward light output ratios (ULOR and DLOR) (7). It is the task of the designer to select a luminaire with properties close to the ideal specification.

The *second stage program* will compute the total installed flux and the minimum number of luminaries of the chosen type to satisfy the appropriate spacing/mounting height ratio (Table 1).

Table 7.1. *Spacing mounting height ratios*

BZ Classification	Ratio
1 and 2	1
3 and 4	1·25
5 to 10	1·5

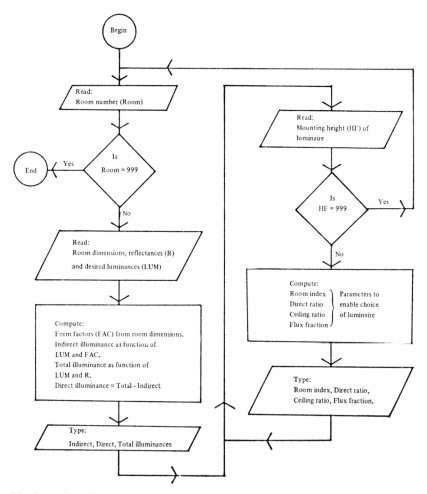

Fig. 7.2. Flow diagram—first stage program.

The designer must now choose the lamps and arrange the lumin-aires in a suitable layout. In many ways this stage is very similar to the lumen method.

The *third stage program* allows the designer to appraise the current solution in terms of the original specification.

The geometric and photometric properties of the chosen instal-

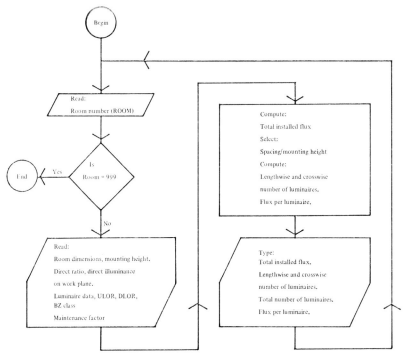

Fig. 7.3. Flow diagram—second stage program.

lation act as inputs to an iterative process which will converge on the average illuminances and luminances for each of the six room surfaces. Since the layout of the luminaires is assumed to be regular and the effects of asymmetry are excluded then the direct illuminance on the four walls will be computed as equal. This may conflict with the output of illuminances from the first stage in cases where the original specification included walls differing in luminances.

Flow charts for the three stages are shown in Figs. 7.2, 7.3 and 7.4, and the listing of the first stage program is given in Appendix 1.

7.3. PROGRAM APPLICATION

7.3.1. Design for an office

The operation of the program suite will be demonstrated by considering the design of the general lighting for an office 12 m long, 6 m

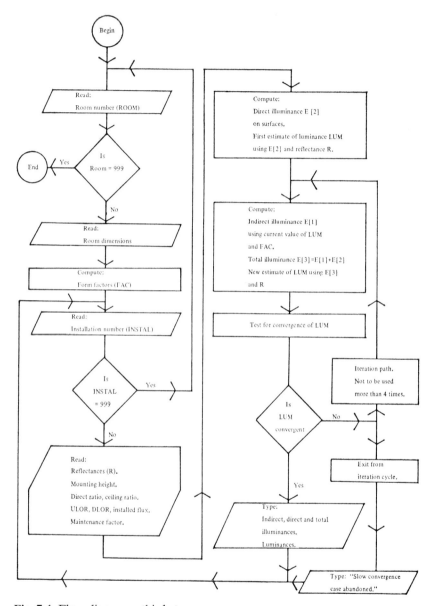

Fig. 7.4. Flow diagram—third stage program.

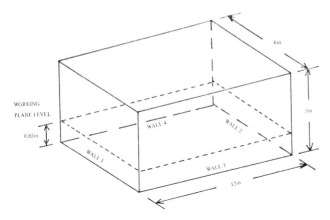

Fig. 7.5. Identity of surfaces.

wide and with a floor to ceiling height of 3 m (Fig. 7.5). The working plane is assumed to be 0·85 m above the floor. The specified luminances and reflectances for the principal surfaces are given in Table 7.2.

Table 7.2. *Specification of luminances and reflectances*

Surface	Wall 1	Wall 2	Wall 3	Wall 4	Ceiling	Working plane
Av. luminance cd/m²	35	35	35	35	27	27*
Av. reflectance	0·50	0·50	0·50	0·50	0·70	0·20

Figure 7.6 shows the computer record for the first stage. Information on dimensions, reflectances and luminances has been input by the designer acting on cues supplied by the computer. Then follows a period of computation to give values of illuminance for each of the surfaces.

In the present examples, the direct, indirect and total illuminances are consistent. However, in other designs, cases have been experienced in which the computed indirect illuminance exceeds the total illuminance. This in turn gives rise to negative direct illuminance with a negative flux fraction. Failures of this nature indicate that the particular luminance/reflectance specification cannot be realised and a practical

* This is equivalent to a working plane total illuminance of 424 lux. At this illuminance a white paper surface with a reflectance of 0·70 (70 per cent) would have a luminance of 94·5 cd/m².

```
DO PART 1
LUMINANCE DESIGN FIRST STAGE
ROOM 21
LENGTH 12.000      WIDTH  6.000      CEILING HT  3.000      WORK HT  0.850

LUMINANCES AND REFLECTANCES
```

	WALL 1	WALL 2	WALL 3	WALL 4	CEILING	WORK
LUM	35.0	35.0	35.0	35.0	27.0	27.0
REF	0.50	0.50	0.50	0.50	0.70	0.20

```
ILLUMINANCES
```

IND	92	92	92	92	95	95
DIR	128	128	128	128	27	330
TOT	220	220	220	220	121	424

```
HEIGHT OF FITTINGS ABOVE FLOOR    3.000
INDEX 1.860     DIRECT RATIO   .705     CEILING RATIO  1.000     FRACTION  .057

HEIGHT OF FITTINGS ABOVE FLOOR    2.500
INDEX 2.424     DIRECT RATIO   .757     CEILING RATIO   .454     FRACTION  .135

HEIGHT OF FITTINGS ABOVE FLOOR    999
```

Fig. 7.6. Computer printout—first stage program.

solution can only be reached by modification of the original specification.

On cue from the computer, the designer will input the height of the luminaire. The output will give the room index, direct ratio, ceiling ratio and flux fraction appropriate to the mounting height. The designer may, if he wishes, consider further mounting heights or he may terminate the first stage by responding with 999 to the computer's cue for height.

For the purposes of this example, the luminaire is assumed to be at or near ceiling height, i.e. mounting height is 3·000 m. The computed properties for the installation are as follows:

Room index 1·860   Ceiling ratio 1·000
Direct ratio 0·705   Flux fraction 0·057

Inspection of the particular combination of room index and direct

DO PART 5
LUMINANCE DESIGN SECOND STAGE

ROOM 21

LENGTH   12.000   WIDTH   6.000   FTG   3.000   WORK HT   0.850

DIRECT RATIO 0.705   WORK PLANE ILLUMINATION   330   MAINT   0.80

FTG REF   3   ULOR   0.03   DLOR   0.43   BZ CLASS   4

INSTALLED FLUX   97971   NUMBER FTGS IN LENGTH   5   IN WIDTH   3

TOTAL NUMBER FTGS   15   FLUX PER FTG   6531

Fig. 7.7. Computer printout—second stage program.

ratio in conjunction with the BZ classification curves (7) establishes that the luminaire should belong to BZ4. A ceiling ratio of 1·000 means that all the upward light from the luminaire must be incident on the ceiling.

At this stage it is necessary for the designer to choose a luminaire to match as closely as possible the installation properties listed above. As a possible solution the luminaire described in Table 7.3 will be considered.

Table 7.3. *Luminaire data*

General description:	Recessed modular unit with shallow opal plastic diffusing dish
BZ classification:	4
ULOR 3 per cent ⎫	Flux fraction 0·07
DLOR 43 per cent ⎭	(3/43)
Luminous area:	4650 cm² for 2 No. 65W tube unit

The BZ class is correct but there is a slight disagreement in the flux fractions. The effect of this discrepancy will be tested in the third stage program.

Input of working plane direct illuminance, maintenance factor, direct ratio and luminaire data into the second stage program (Fig. 7.7)

DO PART 7
LUMINANCE DESIGN THIRD STAGE

ROOM   21
LENGTH   12.000   WIDTH   6.000   CEILING HT   3.000   WORK HT 0.850

INSTALLATION 1
FTG HT   3.000   DIRECT RATIO   0.705   CEILING RATIO   1.000
ULOR   0.03   DLOR   0.43   INSTALLED FLUX 99000   MAINT   0.80

	WALL 1	WALL 2	WALL 3	WALL 4	CEILING	WORK
REF	0.50	0.50	0.50	0.50	0.70	0.20
IND	92	92	92	92	94	95
DIR	130	130	130	130	33	333
TOT	222	222	222	222	127	428
LUM	35.3	35.3	35.3	35.3	28.2	27.3

Fig. 7.8. Computer printout—third stage program.

leads to computed values for installed flux and the minimum number of luminaires. Arranging 15 luminaires in a regular 5 × 3 array and installing 2 No. 65 W natural fluorescent tubes in each luminaire will give:

flux per fitting = 6600 lm
and   total installed flux = 99 000 lm

This arrangement would satisfy the output of the second stage.

The proposed installation is now determined and the third stage program can be entered. The results of the appraisal are shown in Fig. 7.8. A comparison of the luminances from the appraisal with the original specification will show a maximum individual difference of 4·5 per cent and an average difference for the six surfaces of 1·5 per cent.

Use of the luminance design method does not guarantee freedom from glare. The results of a glare index computation using the IES tables (2) gave a value of 16·5 for the installation. This is well within the limiting value of 19 specified by the IES Code.

7.3.2. Exploration of alternative solutions

The application which has been described above progresses steadily through the three stages in sequence. However, it must be noted that

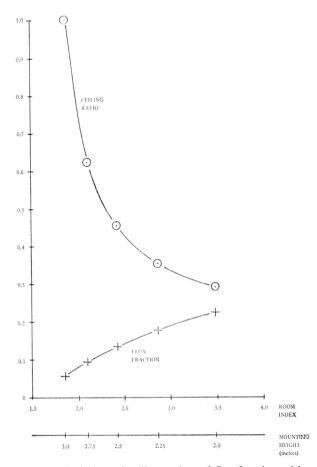

Fig. 7.9. Variation of ceiling ratio and flux fraction with mounting height.

the designer is not debarred from using any one of the stages to study alternative partial solutions. For example, in the first stage, the luminaire properties are determined for a given mounting height. The consequences of choosing alternative heights can be conveniently explored. The results of such an experiment using the basic specification of Section 73.1 are presented in Fig. 7.9 and 7.10.

If the luminance specification is to be maintained then a reduction in the height of the fitting dictates an increase in the flux fraction and

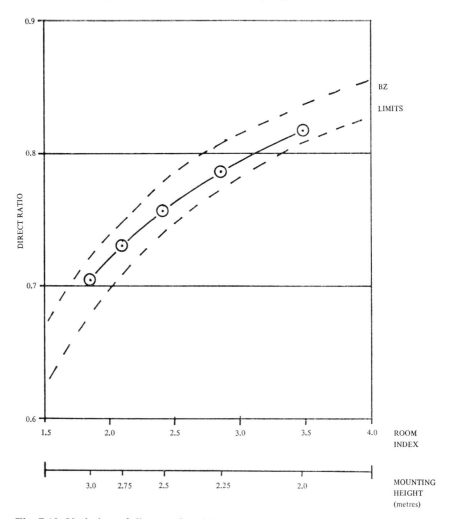

Fig. 7.10. Variation of direct ratio with mounting height.

a reduction in ceiling ratio. The plot of direct ratio against room index falls within the limits for the BZ4 class over the whole of the range of mounting heights from 2·0 m to 3·0 m. If for the sake of argument we assume that the total light output ratio of the luminaire is 50 per cent then the range of properties to cover the variation in heights is given in Table 7.4.

Table 7.4. *Luminaire properties for different mounting heights*

Mounting height (m)	BZ class	ULOR per cent	DLOR per cent
3·0	4	2·5	47·5
2·75	4	4·5	45·5
2·5	4	6·0	44·0
2·25	4	7·5	42·5
2·0	4	9·0	41·0

7.4. CONCLUSION

A suite of computer aided design programs has been written for application in the total appearance or luminance design of interiors. It has been demonstrated that the designer and computer each has a role to play in the design process. The computer can very effectively deal with the lengthy, repetitive calculations that comprise the mathematical model of the design problem while the designer is free to build up and explore a broader range of possible solutions. Time and tedium are no longer factors to be directed against the luminance design methods.

The present computer programs must be extended to handle rooms with surfaces made up of zones of different luminances and rooms free from the length/width restriction. In addition, attention is needed in the provision of a data bank for luminaires and lamps to extend the assistance the computer can give in the choice of luminaires.

REFERENCES

1. *Interior Lighting Design Handbook* (1970) (London: Lighting Industry Federation).
2. ILLUMINATING ENGINEERING SOCIETY (1967). 'Evaluation of discomfort glare: the IES glare index system for artificial lighting installations.' *Technical Report* No. 10 (London: IES). See also: *The IES Code* (1973) (London: IES).
3. WALDRAM, J. M. (1954). 'Studies in interior lighting'. *Trans. Illum. Eng. Soc.* (London) **19** (4), 95–133.

4. HOPKINSON, R. G., (1965). 'A proposed luminance basis for a lighting code.' *Trans Illum. Eng. Soc.* (London) **30** (3), 63–88.

5. COOMBER, D. C. and JAY, P. A. (1967). 'A simplified method of calculation for luminance ratio and designed appearance lighting installations.' *Monograph* No. 10. (London: IES).

6. HISANO, K. (1946). 'Light flux distribution in a rectangular parallelepiped and its simplifying scale'. Illuminating Engineering (USA) **41** (3), 232–247.

7. ILLUMINATING ENGINEERING SOCIETY (1971). 'The calculation of utilization factors. The BZ method'. *Technical Report* No. 2 (London: IES).

APPENDIX 1

```
1.01  TYPE FORM 1
1.02  READ ROOM IN FORM 2
1.03  STOP IF ROOM=999
1.04  READ L,W,HC,HP IN FORM 3
1.05  TYPE #,FORM 4, FORM 5, FORM 6, FORM 5
1.06  READ LUM[1],LUM[2],LUM[3],LUM[4],LUM[5],LUM[6] IN FORM 7
1.07  READ R[1],R[2],R[3],R[4],R[5],R[6] IN FORM 8
1.08  TYPE FORM 5
1.09  A=2*L*W/((L+W)*(HC-HP)),  B=SQRT(A↑2+1),  C=ATN(A,B)
1.10  D=1.41425*ATN(1,1.41425*A)
1.11  F1=LN((2*A↑2+1)/(2*(A↑2+1)))
1.12  F2=LN((2*A↑2+1)/((A↑2+1)↑2))
1.13  FAC1=2*(B*C+D-A*$PI/4-ATN(1,A)-A*F1)/$PI
1.14  FAC2=(4*B*C/A-(4*ATN(A,1))/A-F2/A↑2)/$PI
1.15  FAC3=A*(1-FAC2)/4
1.16  FAC4=(2-2*FAC1-A*(1-FAC2))/4
1.17  X=(LUM[3]+LUM[4])*FAC4+(LUM[5]+LUM[6])*FAC3
1.18  Y=(LUM[1]+LUM[2])*FAC4+(LUM[5]+LUM[6])*FAC3
1.19  Z=(LUM[1]+LUM[2]+LUM[3]+LUM[4])*FAC3/A
1.20  E[1,1]=(LUM[2]*FAC1+X)*$PI
1.21  E[1,2]=(LUM[1]*FAC1+X)*$PI
1.22  E[1,3]=(LUM[4]*FAC1+Y)*$PI
1.23  E[1,4]=(LUM[3]*FAC1+Y)*$PI
1.24  E[1,5]=(LUM[6]*FAC2+Z)*$PI
1.25  E[1,6]=(LUM[5]*FAC2+Z)*$PI
1.26  DO PART 2 FOR Q=1:1:6 FOR P=3
1.27  DO PART 3 FOR S=1:1:6 FOR R=2
1.28  TYPE #,FORM 9, FORM 5
1.29  TYPE E[1,1],E[1,2],E[1,3],E[1,4],E[1,5],E[1,6] IN FORM 10
1.30  TYPE E[2,1],E[2,2],E[2,3],E[2,4],E[2,5],E[2,6] IN FORM 11
1.31  TYPE E[3,1],E[3,2],E[3,3],E[3,4],E[3,5],E[3,6] IN FORM 12
1.32  TYPE FORM 5,#
1.33  READ HF IN FORM 13
1.34  INDEX=L*W/((L+W)*(HF-HP))
1.35  G=(E[2,1]+E[2,2])*W
1.36  H=(E[2,3]+E[2,4])*L
1.37  DIR1=L*W*E[2,6]/(L*W*E[2,6]+(G+H)*(HF-HP))
1.38  DIRUP1=L*W*E[2,5]/(L*W*E[2,5]+(G+H)*(HC-HF))
1.39  FRACT1=DIR1*E[2,5]/(DIRUP1*E[2,6])
1.40  TYPE INDEX,DIR1,DIRUP1,FRACT1 IN FORM 14
1.405 TYPE #
1.41  READ HF IN FORM 13
1.42  TO STEP 1.34 IF NOT HF=999
1.43  TYPE #,#,#,#
1.44  TO STEP 1.02
2.01  E[P,Q]=$PI*LUM[Q]/R[Q]
3.01  E[R,S]=E[3,S]-E[1,S]
```

Listing of the program for the first stage.

APPENDIX 1 (continued)

NOTES ON FORMAT AND SYMBOLS

TYPE	instruction to computer to print (output) items specified.
READ	instruction to read (input) items specified.
STOP	program termination.
DO	instruction to proceed with a section of the program.
FORM	a defined layout for input and output.
L	length of room.
W	width of room.
HC	height of room.
HP	height of working plane.
HF	height of luminaire above floor.
INDEX	room index.
DIR	direct ratio.
FRACT	flux fraction.
DIRUP	ceiling ratio

Illuminances are denoted by notation E [i, j]

$i = 1$ Indirect illuminance
$i = 2$ Direct illuminance
$i = 3$ Total illuminance

$j = 1$ Wall 1
$j = 2$ Wall 2
$j = 3$ Wall 3
$j = 4$ Wall 4
$j = 5$ Ceiling
$j = 6$ Working plane

Thus the direct illuminance on the ceiling is denoted by E [2, 5]

8
Building ergonomics

R. J. Talbot MSc, BSc (Eng), ACGI
Lecturer in Ergonomics,
Design Research Laboratory,
Department of Building,
University of Manchester Institute of Science & Technology

8.1. INTRODUCTION

Ergonomics is a *young* discipline—the word, meaning 'the customs, habits or laws of work', was coined in 1949: and it is concerned with *human performance*, particularly in relation to artefacts, equipment or machines.

These two characteristics have important implications for ergonomists, for people affected by the application (or non-application) of ergonomics expertise, and, not least, for anyone writing about ergonomics.

The focus of study of the discipline suggests that ergonomics knowledge is potentially applicable to any human activity involving the use of artefacts. This gives it a broader scope than many disciplines; it also means that ergonomics knowledge is relevant to most of the established professions and in particular to the design professions. Thus ergonomics is cross-disciplinary in nature, and the application of ergonomics knowledge requires either inter-disciplinary collaboration (if ergonomics is to be regarded as a distinct discipline) or the inclusion of ergonomics in professional and technological education (if it is to be regarded as an integratable area of knowledge). Neither of these is easy to bring about.

Thus the very nature of the subject gives rise to problems of implementation and of understanding. These problems are not made any easier by the fact that ergonomics is of very recent origin. The effects of this are several, but perhaps the most significant is that there is no concensus, even among ergonomists, on several critical aspects of the work. Questions relating to the value of ergonomics, to the relevance of basic human sciences research to application, to methodological issues and to the relative importance of various aspects remain unresolved. This state of affairs is not necessarily a bad thing, of course, since debate, controversy and critical self-appraisal are necessary to the development and growth of any new discipline. It does, however, give rise to general misunderstanding of the nature, purposes, value and relevance of ergonomics to those outside the profession.

A second consequence of the youth of the discipline is that there are not many ergonomists! Thus there are gaps in the existing body of knowledge (with nobody to fill them), there are many as yet unexplored fields of application and an insufficient number of teachers. In other words the ergonomics effort is thinly spread out over parts only of a potentially huge field. For most ergonomists it is necessary to be both innovator and advocate as well as practitioner.

I believe in the ultimate value of ergonomics and also that there is considerable lack of understanding of the subject in the building field. Thus the main purpose of this article is to clear up some of the misunderstanding and to show the relevance of ergonomics to building.

In order to do this, I shall describe ergonomics in general (Section 8.2), give an ergonomists view of building together with an indication of potential and actual applications of ergonomics to building (Section 8.3). Section 8.4 deals with some problems facing ergonomists and parties interested in building, and contains my conclusions on the current situation and on possible future developments.

8.2. ERGONOMICS

8.2.1. Origins and development

Ergonomics is largely a post-war development. Both world wars have in different ways provided considerable stimulation to research on human performance. In the first, the urgent need to produce munitions led to studies of industrial fatigue and working hours, and to research on the related problems of the effects of environmental conditions such as heating, lighting, noise and vibration on human performance. During the Second World War, problems associated with the human operation of military equipment added a further dimension to such work. These problems included difficulties facing pilots of planes flying at increasingly greater speeds and altitudes, the effects of tropical jungles and arctic waters on soldiers and sailors, the handling of guns, tanks and ships and the correct identification of enemy ships and aircraft on the newly developed radar systems. Much of this work required the involvement of human scientists—psychologists, physiologists and anatomists in co-operation with engineers in the design and evolution of new equipment and working conditions necessary for the war effort.

This collaborative work was not only successful, but also mutually satisfying to the groups of scientists and engineers who worked together. It was also believed that such conjoint work could be of considerable importance to industry in peace time. So the concept was developed of studying man in his working environment with the aim of *fitting the job to the worker* in addition to the task of *fitting the worker to the job* by training and selection procedures.

These intentions were formalized with the formation of the Ergonomics Research Society in 1949 and the subsequent publication of the Society's Journal *Ergonomics*. A considerable amount of research was performed by psychologists, physiologists, functional anatomists and others during the early years, but somewhere along the line, the organizational, economic and sociological problems of actually getting this research applied, were neglected and much of the research, though essential to an understanding of problems of man at work, did not find its place in contemporary industrial practice.

The interests of the majority of members of the Society were, as the name suggests, more orientated to research into human behaviour than to direct improvement of the working situation. To be sure a number of individuals and small groups did in the 1950's attempt to apply their ergonomics expertise to industrial problems, but it became clear from their experience that improvement by modification of existing designs was not easy to justify economically and also that existing academic syllabi were not particularly appropriate for this type of work. Rather than merely modify existing designs, it was felt that the ergonomist should be involved from an early stage in the design process, thereby reducing the likelihood of poor ergonomic design and reducing the need for expensive re-thinking of equipment design solutions.

Unfortunately, this solution to the application problem brought its own difficulties with it. Ergonomics education was not suitable for imparting design expertise, and furthermore, equipment design was the prerogative of the traditional disciplines of engineering, architecture and industrial design. The movement concerned with developing systematic design methods had not really got off the ground at this time, so there wasn't even a conceptual basis for integrating ergonomics information in design. It should be stated, that despite these difficulties, there were many examples of useful ergonomic contributions in industry. These examples were, however, more a function of the skill of the people involved than of any particular virtue of the ergonomic approach in general. What appeared to be needed was an understanding by the ergonomist of what he had to offer and to whom, and what his own place was in the developing scheme of things. In other words he needed a philosophy.

In this context, the American publications expounding a 'systems' point of view which began to appear in the mid 1950's were seen by some as the answer to the ergonomists prayer. Some practitioners embraced the systems concept and developed the *Systems Ergonomics Approach*. However, many academic members of the Society did not (and still don't) believe in or use this approach, so that a schism developed between the systems men and what they disparagingly referred to as 'the knobs and dials' brigade. Just as the systems approach was getting off the ground in Britain, disturbing signs that all was not well with developments in America began to appear. It became clear by the mid-sixties that the systems approach was not flourishing in military work (the main area of ergonomics or *human factors* work in the USA) nor was it percolating into the industrial field either. The reasons for these difficulties were partly a function of the American set-up and partly a function of the then 'state of the art' of systems thinking. Considerable theoretical advances have been made since then, and there are many examples of successful uses of the systems approach. However, there are still significant gaps between theory and practice at the present time.

So far, I have been describing the military origins, the early history and the problems of industrial ergonomics. The purpose of all this is to give an impression of the diversity of the field of ergonomics and to illustrate the difficulty of giving a definitive description of the discipline. To complete this picture it is necessary to describe recent developments in applications of ergonomics. I refer in particular to non-military, non-industrial applications, that is the ergonomics of everyday life. In our modern developed society people interact with man-made artefacts almost continuously and there is a huge field of potential application of ergonomics knowledge in such areas as education, health, travel, public services, entertainment and leisure, communications and so on.

Further, as concern is growing for the deprived and less well off sections of the population, the need for ergonomics for the disabled and the old in particular is growing. Increasing attention is also being given to problems of working and living in the home (a serious source of accidents) and to problems of road safety. In general, people seem less prepared to tolerate bad design and poor environments than hitherto. In principle, there is no limit to the scope of ergonomics. It may be that this latest development is the most appropriate subject for ergonomic study, since social values are sometimes regarded as more important than economic necessity.

8.2.2. Ergonomists

Not only is there tremendous variety in the fields of potential application of ergonomics but also in ergonomists. No two ergonomists are alike. Although people with human sciences backgrounds—psychologists, physiologists, anatomists etc.—are in the majority there is a considerable proportion of ergonomists with engineering, architectural, product design, management science and social science origins. More significantly there has been in recent years a considerable growth in the number of young people who read ergonomics as their first degree. Also, many universities and polytechnics include ergonomics in their undergraduate and postgraduate courses in a wide range of subjects.

Ergonomists participate in design, research and development work in military establishments—related to aircraft, ships, land vehicles, space vehicles and submarines and undersea experimental habitats; they are involved in industry (both private and public sectors), in the design of products, capital equipment, production processes and the working environment. They work for government departments such as the postal, telephone, rail and health services. Some work for or are sponsored by the various Research Councils—Medical Research Council, Social Science Research Council and Agriculture. Others work for Local Government, charitable foundations (particularly on the problem of the aged and the disabled) and University departments. Many ergonomists act as consultants covering most of these interests.

It is probably fair to say that the majority of ergonomists are inclined more to research work than to application and design but there does seem to be considerable growth in these latter areas. Interest in systematic design methods and the study of designers at work is also on the increase.

Such a variety of backgrounds, jobs and interests among ergonomists makes it somewhat difficult to present any definitive statement of the aims, methods and content of ergonomics. So what follows is inevitably biassed by my own preferences, experience and knowledge, although I have tried to be as representative as possible.

8.2.3. Aims and definitions of ergonomics

Over the years many versions of the aims and definitions of ergonomics have been given. Edholm (1) calls it the *biological study of man at work*. Fucigna (2) states: *the ultimate objective of ergonomics is to maximize job performance and job satisfaction within the constraints imposed by available resources and the 'givens' in a particular situation*. Van Wely (3) suggests that the general aim of ergonomics is *to promote the efficiency, comfort and health of man in his working environment*. Beevis and Slade (4) emphasize *increase in productivity, reduction of accidents and improvements in the working environment*. The U.S. Military Standard 1472 indicates that the purposes of human factors (the more psychology-orientated American equivalent of the British ergonomics) should be *to achieve satisfactory performance, to reduce skill requirements, to reduce training time, to increase reliability and to foster design standardization*; and adds *designing work methods, equipment and environment to suit capacities of users greatly improves their performance, comfort and health*. On the front page of *Ergonomics*, ergonomics is described as 'the scientific study of human performance and human factors in work, machine control and equipment design'. Likewise, the subtitle of the newer *Applied Ergonomics Journal* is 'Man—machine—environment—systems technology'.

This last definition although just about the shortest is the most comprehensive, since it is not restrictive to man-at-war or man-at-work. It also highlights the technological nature of ergonomics and I believe that ergonomics has to be a technology based upon, but not dominated by, scientific knowledge of human beings.

The overall goals of ergonomics are: (a) to improve the effectiveness of the man-machine system and therefore of the group, organization or community to which the man belongs (effectiveness here is taken to mean achievement of specified objectives); (b) to promote the well being of the human being through reduction of the likelihood of accidents, discomfort and health risks and, by so doing; (c) to help bring about a revaluation of the special qualities, abilities and needs of human beings.

Most ergonomists would agree with the first two goals, but there is less widespread support for the third. Ergonomists have for some time been aware of the fact that human beings have special attributes not reproducible by machines, and that there are therefore both disadvantages in and limits to the degree to which processes can be mechanized and automated. Bowen (5) says ' . . . we cannot be successful in utilizing the resources of man in a system until we accept that he contributes a qualitatively different form of operation in comparison to machine elements. He operates adaptively and has the capability of managing whatever resources the system affords him to meet the challenges of the situation. Seldom are the challenges completely anticipated'. On the question of automation, Meister (6) suggests that 'Preference for a machine solution to the design problem may lead to

a. higher degree of automation.
b. higher reliability of operations.
c. higher cost.
d. lowered producibility.
e. lowered maintainability.

Preference for operator-based solutions may lead to

a. lowered degree of automation.
b. lowered reliability in operation.
c. lower cost.
d. higher producibility.
e. higher maintainability.'

There are also indications from outside ergonomics that concentration on the first two objectives may be somewhat misguided.

Davis and Taylor (7) describe the rapidly growing body of work on Job Design, wherein three main aspects are emphasised:

1. Task and job rationalization.
2. Job content.
3. Role content.

Time and motion study, work simplification, improvement, management and parts of ergonomics are the main contributors to task and job rationalization. The principles of worker satisfaction, job enrichment and job enlargement contribute to work on job content, while job design, socio-technical systems, group dynamics and general systems theory are the major influences on work on role content. Davis and Taylor, in their Introduction, say 'At present, the three strands of development described in this introduction exist concurrently. Since we live in a society that is organized partly on industrial and partly on post-industrial models, it is not inappropriate that all three strands should co-exist. However, given the accelerating changes in technology and the social environment, it is probable that appropriate applications of the task and job rationalization strand, will diminish in the future, and that it will become increasingly dysfunctional'.

Several speakers at the recent Loughborough Conference on *The Environment in Buildings* (September, 1972) advocate the replacing of man at the centre of our considerations. Ryan (8) for example suggests that '. . . what we have to recognize is this, that industrialists preoccupied with economics, profit and loss, diminishing returns, increased production, and architects and engineers preoccupied in their turn with abstract design factors, modular planning, stresses, materials, costs per square foot and so on, are all losing sight of the real basis of their problems—that is the human factor. Whatever, the purpose of a building, men use it, and unless it is designed with 'man in mind' in the sense we have been discussing (i.e. the preservation of a man's sense of competence in his work) it will always fall short of its goal.'

Grall (9) in a paper on *Environmental Design and Research for the Non-Ambulatory*, states that: 'truly consumer-oriented design is often safer and readily interacted with by all, the young, aged and disabled included'. Perhaps Langdon (10) puts it best of all: '. . . human sciences have almost universally been applied to problems resulting from building technology or administrative requirements. There is little evidence of initiative on the part of human sciences themselves to produce in a conscious fashion a fully human environment, one based on the study of social and psychological goals and functions. Nor have such studies concerned themselves overmuch with aesthetic

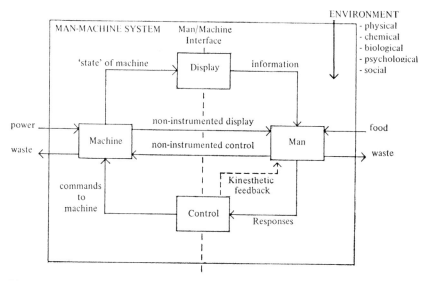

Fig. 8.1. The man-machine system

Fig. 8.2. A simple information processing model of the human operator.

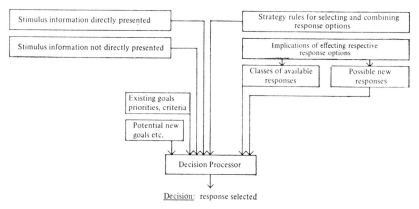

Fig. 8.3. Decision-making: classes of information required (after Miller, 56)

or hedonic aspects. On the contrary, they have been directed mainly to improvements in task-related effectiveness.'

Thus it is not, in my view sufficient for ergonomists to concern themselves only with effectiveness and well-being of people within existing situations but also, by virtue of their special knowledge of human capabilities to contribute to a human sciences initiative to place man back at the centre of the technologists' considerations.

(If this foregoing discussion seems to the reader to be more related to what ergonomics should be rather than what it is, let me remind him that ergonomics is essentially what people—ergonomists in particular—say it is and that it is still a rapidly changing discipline).

So far I have dealt with the origins and development of ergonomics, with the nature of ergonomists and with the aims of ergonomics. These considerations have been at a somewhat general level. In order to complete the picture it is necessary to describe the work and interests of the ergonomist at a more detailed level. I shall give few if any examples of ergonomic work in this section since I intend to do that in Section 8.3 when considering the relevance of ergonomics to building.

8.2.4. The focal point for study

At the centre of the ergonomist's consideration is the 'man-machine system'. Fig. 8.1 is a representation of this system showing the information pathways within the system, and interactions between the system and its environment.

The human being receives information from the machine through his senses from instrumented displays or directly from the machine. He also receives information from the environment. This information is interpreted by the human being and he uses this interpretation to decide what actions, if any, need to be taken (Fig. 8.2). The sort of factors affecting his decisions also include his knowledge of possible actions and their likely effects, his understanding of the purposes of the system and of any rules, instructions or orders which might be provided to guide him (Fig. 8.3).

He may then carry out his chosen actions by operating the controls of the machine. The machine will (or should) change its state as a result of this control action and thereby cause new information to be shown on the display(s) which is again perceived and interpreted by the operator and so on.

It is quite easy to see how this model can be applied to say a vehicle. Consider a vehicle going up a hill. The driver receives several information inputs—the slope of the incline, the sound of the engine, the speed of the vehicle, the change in speed of the vehicle. He may also have information relating to the performance of the vehicle on hills (or even on the particular hill he's climbing at the time), he will have information from the environment—wind speed and direction, surface conditions, location of other vehicles etc. He can use all of this information to decide if and when he needs to change gear. He will also be familiar with the consequences of not changing gear or not timing the change correctly etc. If he does decide to change gear he has to locate and operate the gear lever, the clutch and the accelerator pedal all in a particular sequence (and he may be aware of the consequences of getting the sequence or timing wrong). These are the controls which change the state of the vehicle—i.e. its speed mainly. The new state of the vehicle is displayed to the driver through instruments, through engine pitch etc. and through observation of the outside environment through the windscreen. This is not a complete description of all that is involved in the task, but it serves to illustrate the use of the model.

The man-machine system concept can be used for situations other than vehicle operation, of course. Numerous examples come to mind including using a telephone, opening doors or windows, typewriting, using calculating machines, slide rules, log tables, operating lathes, cement mixers, cranes and so on, *ad infinitum.*

Some of these examples don't involve instrumented display of information e.g. opening windows, or controls which are attached to the machine e.g. using a slide rule or log tables. Nevertheless, the same principles of operation can be shown to exist. Each task involves taking in information, interpreting it, making decisions and performing some action as a consequence of the decision. That is, the precise mode of information display may vary as may the means of effecting action, but the model remains appropriate for describing what's going on.

This model not only gives us a framework for analysing and describing the behaviour of a man-machine combination, but also requires that, if we wish to modify the system or design a new version, we must ask questions such as:

1. What is the man-machine system supposed to achieve?

2. What are the respective roles of man and machine?

3. What task or tasks does the man have to perform, in what sequence and with what results? How do these relate to the overall objectives?

4. What skills and abilities, both mental and physical, are required of the human being in order to perform his tasks/actions?

5. What influence is there on the operator's decisions and actions of:

displays   —sensory input to the operator;

controls   —motor output from the operator;

display-control—relations between displays and associated controls?
    layouts

6. What is the influence on the man's position, posture and reach of such things as machine size, chairs, desks, adjacent machines, structures, material etc?

7. What are the influences upon behaviour and performance of the physical, chemical, biological, psychological and social aspects of the environment?

physical: light and colour, noise, heat, vibration etc.

chemical: gas, liquid, pressure, smell etc.

biological: microbes, insects, animals, flora.

psychological: work team, command structure, shift conditions, discomfort or risk.

social: norms of behaviour, social needs/drives.

8. What unusual conditions may arise?

e.g. emergencies, extreme environmental conditions etc.

We ask these types of questions so that we can predict the likelihood of or prevent the occurrence of certain eventualities. These, in order of increasing seriousness of their consequences are:

1. delay in accomplishment of the purpose or goal of the system or man.

2. failure to accomplish this purpose.

3. equipment malfunction, so that not only is the purpose not achieved, but also the capability of accomplishment is lost.

4. hazard to own or other's safety.

Now these failures can all be put down to human error (which can be defined as a deviation from some specified objective) either during design, production, operation or maintenance etc. of the system. Some errors are identified as such only in retrospect of course: for example, the fatigue failures of the Comet aircraft were not predicted because so little was known about the metal fatigue phenomenon. It is sometimes difficult to locate the source of other errors particularly in those industries where design and production are closely inter-related. In other words this generalization with respect to human error is not entirely adequate. However, it does give me a basis for pointing out that ergonomists are able in many instances to make contributions which reduce the probability of the occurrence of all these types of error.

First of all he, like everybody else, accepts the possibility of human error. In the words of Meister (6) 'He assumes, however, that error is not inevitable, is not the consequence of human (operator) 'fallibility'. The assumption is made that error occurs only when the conditions exist which predispose the human to make the error'. Insofar as it is possible to control these conditions, error can be prevented. Answers to the eight questions listed above give the ergonomist information on which to base recommendations for design or modification of equipment, workspace, environment, or for training and selection of operators. These recommendations should lead to a reduction in human error and decrease the likelihood of occurrence of the four types of failure given above.

We will conclude this section on ergonomics with a closer look at the different types of error committed by the main parties concerned with man-machine systems, namely designers, producers, operators/ users and maintainers of man-machine systems.

Designer errors   —designing something difficult to produce.
                      —designing something not according to brief.
                      —designing something difficult to use even in ideal circumstances.
                      —failure to design for a wide enough range of users.
                      —failure to take into account interactions with other systems.

	—failure to design for an adequate range of environmental conditions.
Producer errors	—producing something which doesn't work adequately.(workmanship errors, inspection errors)
	—requiring people to work in inadequate conditions with inadequate equipment. (management errors)
	—letting product designer errors go through.
Operator or user errors	—using the equipment inappropriately (errors of commission).
	—failure to perform correct actions (errors of omission).
	—out of sequence use, or incorrect timing of actions.

Maintenance errors—failure to correctly diagnose problems, failure to repair defects.

A fifth category could be added, namely *legislative or government error*

—failure to legislate against error pre-disposing conditions.

—failure to implement the legislation that does exist.

—failure to realise the contribution the ergonomist can make.

This addition raises the issue of responsibility for improving the design of man-machine environment systems in general, and for implementing improvements.

Very often it is in the interests of one or more of the directly interested parties to implement changes. Occasionally however, government legislation is required. One of the key problems lies in identifying the need for changes. A significant difficulty here is the fact that man is a highly adaptable animal and he can learn to adjust to the demands placed upon him. Thus problems or inadequacies in design tend to be overlooked or relegated in importance. He *can* operate badly designed machines, he *can* tolerate bad or awkward postures, he *can* learn to use difficult tools, he *can* operate in uncomfortable, unsafe, unhealthy environmental conditions. But he does not operate at his maximum effectiveness and is much more prone to error and accidents especially in emergency and high stress situations.

It is obvious to an ergonomist that poorly designed displays will be difficult to read, that badly located controls will be awkward to use, that poor posture can cause disability through backache or lead to joint damage and arthritis. But it is not always so obvious to the designer, the producer or often to the user himself. It is the responsibility of the ergonomist, therefore, to point these things out in such a way that improvements will be made.

8.3. ERGONOMICS AND BUILDING

8.3.1. Introduction

Ergonomics, then, is concerned with interactions in the'man-machine-systems-environment' area. It has applications in all walks of life. Because of its origins in the study of men-at-war, and its extension to man-at-work the emphasis in ergonomic studies has been on the *effectiveness* of human performance. Since its more recent permeation into problems of everyday living, and also as a result of the growing realization that man-at-work cannot be treated merely as a machine component, increasing consideration is being given to organizational, social and cultural factors. For the ergonomist the focus of interest is still the man-machine system, even though he may be studying it in a broader context than hitherto.

It is the purpose of this section to indicate the relevance of what ergonomists do to building. First there follows a short description of an ergonomist's view of building, after which a selection of building ergonomics work is described.

8.3.2. An ergonomics view of building

Before describing ergonomics applications in building it is first necessary to be somewhat more explicit on what is meant by the term *building*. As an ergonomist I look at building from the point of view of the people involved.

First there are the people who use buildings—they live in buildings, they work in buildings or they visit buildings to obtain some kind of service.

Other people involved with completed buildings include maintainers, repairers, modifiers, removers and installers of equipment of all kinds, firemen and finally those who demolish buildings.

Another major group of people involved in building are those concerned with producing buildings. Their activities range from pre-design (finance, brief, tendering etc.), through design to the actual task of construction.

Building ergonomics is concerned essentially with the human factors involved in these processes of production, service-in-use and use of buildings. Clearly, building ergonomics could be a subject of very broad scope indeed. There are many types of building and a high variety of activities carried out as part of living, working and receiving services associated with these buildings; many of these activities involve the use of artefacts, equipment or machines in spaces within buildings, and require differing degrees of environmental control for their performance; the people who engage in these activities also vary considerably in their physical and mental characteristics and as a consequence place differing demands on buildings, installations and equipment. There is also a high variety of service-in-use activities and user requirements related with buildings. A similar diversity of people, activities, equipment, materials and environment exists for the building production process.

Clearly there is not the space to discuss the whole field of building ergonomics in this article. What follows therefore, is a description of a selection only of ergonomics work related to building. Reference should also be made to Page (11).

8.3.3 Ergonomics for users of buildings

I earlier identified three basic types of use of buildings
—as a dwelling place
—as a work place
—as a place in which to receive services of various kinds.

In the home, several areas are increasingly claiming the attention of ergonomists. In particular the housewife's job has come under scrutiny. For example Ward (12) of the Institute for Consumer Ergonomics, Loughborough argues that if household installations and equipment are in accord dimensionally with the user, if the operation of equipment and performance of tasks is within the physiological compass of the housewife, if equipment is both safe and easy to control, and if environmental factors such as noise, heat and light are kept within specifiable bounds, then she (the housewife) will be able to fulfil her role more effectively, will have more time for leisure activities or for gainful employment and will be less prone to accidents or ill-health arising from her work in the home. More detailed studies of kitchen working surface heights (13 and 14), domestic stairways (15 and 16) doors (17), vision through window-shading materials (18) and heart rate and daily activities of women and children (19) are but a small sample of the ergonomics work relating to dwelling design.

Another area of growing concern is the dwelling requirements of the aged. Mendick (20) surveyed a block of old people's flats and revealed a considerable number of incompatibilities between the occupants and their homes. Storage cupboards not used because they were too high for small arthritic old ladies to reach, windows not openable (or closeable if open) for similar reasons, windows placed just too high in the wall to allow a comfortable view of the neighbourhood from an armchair, inaccessible lift buttons, inadequate heating and poorly designed supports in bathroom and wc etc. were some of the deficiencies uncovered by this study. There is clearly a need for ergonomic consideration of the needs of the elderly.

Another group of users for whom dwelling design is critical are the disabled, particularly wheelchair users (9, 21, 22, 23) and the blind (24).

The wheelchair-bound face particular difficulties in moving about the home (and getting in and out) and in having to perform many activities in a sitting position with equipment which is usually used standing.

The disabled also experience difficulty in connection with public buildings (i.e. buildings to which they go for some service or other) such as offices, banks, cinemas, public conveniences and churches etc. There are problems of access, circulation (both vertical and horizontal), reach and visibility for the wheelchair bound and so on. Goldsmith (23) discusses the problems of designing buildings for the disabled, highlighting difficulties of providing for a wide range of users (including the disabled), conflicts between economic criteria and the requirements of the handicapped, conflicts between the disabled and the 'normal' population, and conflicts between ambulant handicapped and wheelchair users' requirements. Incidentally he defines the disabled as *those people who on account of physical impairment would be*

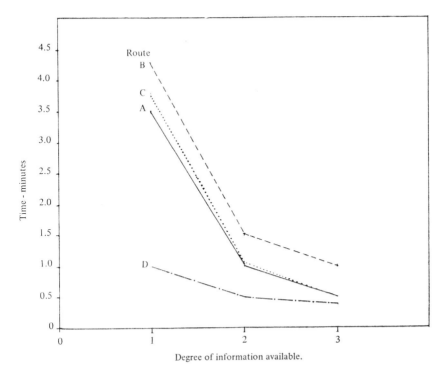

Degree of information available.

1. Subjects unfamiliar with building (present directing system.)

2. Subjects unfamiliar with building (proposed system.)

3. Subject completely familiar with building

Fig. 8.4. Degree of information and time needed to complete a route (Corlett et al, 1972)

handicapped in their use of conventionally designed buildings by the lack of suitable facilities.

For the non-disabled too there are often handicaps in the use of conventionally designed buildings. For example, Best (25) found that many people had difficulties in locating Local Government departments in a large provincial town hall. Because the shape of the building was unusual (trapezoid in plan), because some floors had corridors all round while others had corridors partly blocked off, and particularly because direction signs were badly sited and poorly designed,

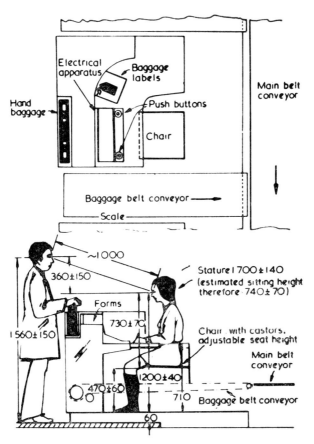

Fig. 8.5. Work place with sitting employee and standing female or male passenger. Dimenisons (mean $\pm 2 \times$ standard deviation) in mm (de Jong, 1927)

people trying to locate various offices took longer than was necessary, or deviated from the shortest possible route with great frequency. Some people interviewed on leaving the building said they had given up and would come back and try again when they had more time. It is quite possible to improve direction-finding in buildings by observing people's behaviour, by locating signs so that they will be noticed, by designing the lettering according to standard ergonomic practice and by giving the user en-route information as to his progress. Corlett *et al*

(26) applied Best's recommendations to a university building and showed significantly improved direction finding performance with the new system (Fig. 8.4).

There are many other areas of ergonomic interest related to 'service' buildings. A common feature of many of these buildings is some sort of counter across which the user and employee communicate. de Jong (27) describes the design and layout of a baggage check-in work station, for Amsterdam Airport, where careful attention was given to the body dimensions of (standing) passengers with their luggage and of the (seated) check-in girl (Fig. 8.5). The layout of the work station influenced to a marked degree the layout of that part of the building.

Poyner (28) describes a study into the effects of anti-bandit screens on communication across post office counters. By observation and interview he showed that a loss of audibility, a reduction in social communication across the counter and a slight deterioration in the public's attitude to the post office resulted following the introduction of anti-bandit screens. In a survey of the behaviour of door users (another common feature of service buildings). Webster (29) discovered numerous inadequacies in the design and arrangements of doors. Poor labelling, difficulties in opening, problems for people with prams, packages or shopping bags were some of the more obvious inadequacies observed. So far only fairly common attributes of service buildings have been considered. When we look at particular types of such buildings—schools, hospitals, cinemas, shops, for example—an even wider range of ergonomics interests becomes apparent, both in terms of specialized equipment (school desks, audio-visual aids, hospital beds, dentists' chairs, cinema seating, shop counters etc.) and also in relation to specific requirements for environmental control. Only space limitations prevent us from opening this particular Pandora's box.

In the preceding paragraph it will have been noticed that I have not been entirely rigorous in sustaining the distinction between people who visit a building for service and the people who work in that building. This is not terribly important since it is only a distinction and not a separation of these two types of building user (their needs must be considered together). However, there are many types of people who work in buildings and who don't come into contact with the service-hungry public. These include office workers, factory workers, laboratory researchers and so on. To describe the vast range of ergonomics related to these people-at-work is not possible in any detail in these pages and is done better in the several books now available on the subject. (See Bibliography. General references). Perhaps the titles of the chapters of the Applied Ergonomics Handbook Part 1 (*Applied Ergonomics* Vol. 1 No. 1 to Vol 2 No. 4) will be sufficient to give the flavour of industrial ergonomics. These are:

1. The Industrial Use of Ergonomics
2. Instruments and People
3. Displays
4. Controls
5. Layout of Panels and Machines
6. Layout of Workspaces
7. Seating in Industry.
8. Thermal Comfort in Industry
9. Noise in Industry
10. Lighting of Workplaces
11. Inspection and Human Efficiency
12. Ergonomics versus Accidents
13. Design of Work for the Disabled
14. Work Organization
15. Systems Design

This concludes our brief look at ergonomics for building users. We will now turn our attention to building construction.

8.3.4. Ergonomics for building construction

Building construction is a mainly outdoor occupation involving a great deal of movement and placing of heavy and often rough materials in all types of weathers, frequently at comparatively great heights, and often in restricted or obstructed spaces. There are a number of aspects of construction work of interest to the ergonomist. There is a great deal of work in the ergonomics literature concerning the effects of the environment on human performance, most of which has indirect relevance to building, as well as reports of studies related directly with construction environmental problems. Pratt (30), presenting the case for paying more attention to the problems of winter building, indicates the several effects of rain, wind, cold and snow on construction. Included in his lists are such effects as *causes discomfort to personnel, increases site hazards, reduces protection offered by horizontal covers, makes steel erection, roofing, wall sheeting, scaffolding hazardous, increases transportation hazards, impedes movement of labour.*

Ergonomics has much to offer in mitigating these effects. Basic research can identify particular effects of adverse weather conditions on human performance. For example, Macworth's work (31) on finger numbness showed that the effects of raising wind speed from still air to only a few miles per hour are just as important in affecting performance as lowering air temperature by 5°C. Combinations of high winds and materials of high thermal diffusivity, coupled with impairment of balance at temperatures below 15°C (32), can lead to increased probability of materials handling errors. Teichner (33) has also shown that reaction times are longer in the cold which might turn a slight error into a serious accident. Cold also has undesirable effects on gripping strength (34) and water reduces coefficient of friction between surfaces.

All these factors affect the effectiveness and safety of human performance, and if we know of the reasons for increased site hazards, we are part way towards solving environmental problems. Poulton (35) discusses the limits within which working environments should be maintained and lists these limits in a table. He shows that when the limits are exceeded there is likely to be a fall in efficiency, an increased susceptibility to accidents and a reduced attendance at work. He reveals the main problem connected with environmental control which is that in many cases the percentage loss in performance cannot be given, thus making it difficult to estimate the cost of sub-optimum environments. Wilkinson (36) describes methods and problems related to assessing the effects of environmental stress on productivity and recommends the employment or consultation of ergonomists to management who suspect they have environmental problems. (An important part of an ergonomist's education is the training he receives in methods of research and investigation. These include field and laboratory experimental design, observational techniques, interviews and questionnaires, simulation techniques and the use of mock-ups as well as specialized electrophysiological techniques for measuring muscle action, eye movements and so on).

Several studies concern manual handling and lifting of weights (37–39), Bobbert (40) performed a detailed study on the optimal form and dimensions of handgrips on concrete building blocks, showing that designing the grips in accordance with dimensions of the hand reduced the physiological work load and increased the maximal lifting power appreciably. Garrett (41) surveys several studies related to the anthropometry and biomechanics of the human hand. Other studies have investigated various methods of carrying loads (42) and force perception in pushing trolleys (43). At an Ergonomics Research Society Industrial Section meeting on *Human Factors in Materials Handling* (44), Troup surveyed the problems of manual handling, arguing that '.... an understanding of the physiology of lifting, pushing, pulling and other manual activities is essential if work is to be so organized that the safety of the population at risk is minimized and that the physical stresses involved are within the range of individual working capacity'.

At the same conference Wadsworth spoke about the factors involved in the design of control units for cranes and excavators. His criteria for good design included: good visibility, comfort, avoidance of undue stretching and exertion, adequate location and design of visual displays, layout and construction to facilitate inspection and normal maintenance, safety and commercial viability. That these criteria (and others) are not met in construction materials handling machinery was demonstrated by Corlett and White (45) in their survey of tower cranes and in a more limited study of a grader by Arkell *et al* (46). Improvements in the ergonomics of crane design are reported in Conran (47) and in Wimpey News (48). An improved dumper has also recently been designed at Loughborough University.

Clearly there is a lot of scope for ergonomic consideration of both environmental problems and manual and mechanical materials handling. A further and major field of work for the ergonomist lies in the study and prevention of accidents (not only during building construction but also in building use.)

In a sense the ergonomist is peculiarly suited to accident investigation. He has basic knowledge of human characteristics (physiological, psychological and anatomical in particular), of human behaviour (particularly in stressful, fatiguing or boring situations) and of the ways (desirable and undesirable) in which man interacts with machine, workspace and environment. He also has a foot in several other camps—engineering, design, management, social psychology—to name but a few. He is unlikely, therefore, to be in a hurry to identify as causes of accidents what are very often only symptoms, and he is most likely to recommend a broad-based approach to the prevention of accidents rather than concentrate on a small selection of methods.

Sell (49) describes in some detail how the consideration during machine design of natural behaviour and human limitations of operators can reduce accidents in industry. His position on accidents is illustrated by the following quotation: 'When an enquiry is held to investigate an injury or accident, one aim is usually to determine responsibility. Such enquiries are normally restricted to those immediately concerned and do not look beyond to the manufacturer or designer of the plant concerned. When they do, the main emphasis is generally on the need to provide such things as guards and other apparatus, which prevent injuries but not the initial errors'. He then goes on to discuss accidents caused by operator forgetfulness (and recommends the building in of some sort of memory system into the machine), by operator expectations being incorrect such as may happen when a driver transfers from one vehicle to another with a different control layout, by overloading a man's information-handling capacity, by a man underestimating the risk of an accident, by errors of judgement, by failing to design for man's perceptual limitations or physical limitations, and by expecting men to work in stressful environments. He gives examples of accidents arising from these causes and in each case measures that can be taken by the designers of equipment, workspace and environment are described. His most important argument is that responsibility for accidents must at least in part, be shared by designers, especially when the (ergonomics) knowledge required to avoid many of them is available.

Singleton (50) also draws attention to the problem of responsibility for human error. To quote: 'There are considerable attitude problems in this area, some of them based on society at large and some of them on individual reactions. For example, most societies have not resolved the distinction between two main approaches. One assumes that human beings are responsible for the errors they make. The opposite view is that errors are an inherent component in all human performance, that they should be planned for and designed for and

P.C.S.T.—15

Objective (actual)   Subjective (estimated)

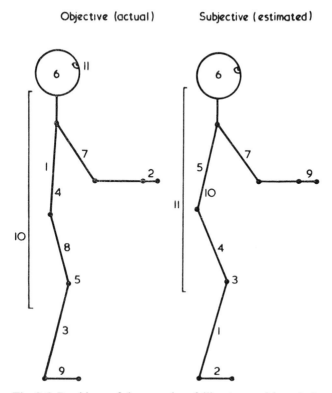

Fig. 8.6. Rankings of danger when felling trees with a chainsaw (Singleton 1950). Operatives' subjective ranking of danger zones does not correlate with what actually happens.

when they do occur the fault should be traced to the system designer rather than the operator. At the individual level, few people are sufficiently self-confident to deliberately acknowledge their own mistakes, particularly if there are financial consequences in doing so. This is an especially difficult problem in the insurance world, where accidents are investigated with a view to deciding who is going to pay for the damage caused either to people or to property. In such a situation is it not surprising to find that it is impossible to regard the evidence as scientific in any sense.'

Another problem relating to error investigation is that there is little correlation between operator action and the consequences for the system. In other words, the operator can sometimes get away with dangerous actions while at other times *trivial* mistakes can have disastrous effects. Despite these problems, there is a noticeable increase in error studies in the ergonomics world, particularly in Singleton's department at the University of Aston. Singleton's article in *Applied Ergonomics* describes this work. After reviewing attempts to classify errors, emphasising the distinction between causes, effects and remedies, also between system and human problems, he considers analytical techniques. These include statistical, critical incident and observation methods. Remedies proposed include better displays and controls, improved monitoring and supervision of performance, and incentives. He describes examples of error research in forestry (Fig. 8.6), keyboard operations related to computer use and power station control rooms. During my perusal of the building literature I have come across many references to construction site accidents but so far I have discovered no sources which advocate an ergonomics-based approach. If the success of error studies in other industries is anything to go by it would seem that it is an approach worth trying in building.

8.4. CONCLUDING REMARKS

A significant event for the future of ergonomics occurred recently with the establishment at the British Standards Institute of four Sub-Committees of the Advisory Committee on Ergonomics and Anthropometrics, which will be concerned with

1. Anthropometry
2. Ergonomics of Consumer Durables
3. Ergonomics of Buildings, Fittings and Furniture
4. Ergonomics of Industrial and Commercial Machinery and Equipment.

Clearly ergonomics is here to stay. It will continue to find application in military, industrial and everyday situations. There is a growing amount of work related to building of which we have seen a sample in the previous section. Much of this work is basic research, however, and is only slowly finding its way into use. Although there are many problems still to be solved concerning implementation of ergonomics principles, there are encouraging signs that the corner is being turned.

To conclude this article I shall identify some of these problems and indicate ways in which they could be or are being overcome.

First there is the problem of integration of ergonomics information in design. This problem has a number of components: a considerable proportion of ergonomics work is more useful for understanding human behaviour in general than it is for utilization by designers. i.e. there is a strong research bias. Chapanis (51), for example, compares typical dependent measures used in ergonomic research with the criteria by which system performance is judged:

Experimental criteria	Systems criteria
Accuracy (or conversely, errors)	Anticipated life of the system
Cardiovascular responses	Appearance
Critical flicker fusion	Comfort
EEG	Convenience
Energy expenditure	Ease of operation or use
Muscle tension	Familiarity
Psychophysical thresholds	Initial cost
Ratings (e.g. of annoyance, comfort)	Maintainability (e.g. mean time to repair)
Reaction time	Manpower requirements
Respiratory responses	Operating cost
Spare mental capacity	Reliability (e.g. mean time to failure)
Speed	Safety
Trials to learn	Training requirements

Clearly it is difficult to identify the correspondence between the two sets of performance measures. What's suitable for the laboratory may not be directly relevant to the real system. The situation is not hopeless, of course. Ergonomics research data can be used to specify limiting conditions (35), there is a growing body of applied ergonomics work relating directly to systems criteria and the advent of error investigation looks as though it may provide a unifying framework for research and application.

A second related component of the integration problem is the relative ignorance among ergonomists of the design process, of the ways in which designers use information and of the best methods of presenting information for designers to use. There are encouraging signs that these difficulties may be overcome. There is growing interest among design methods researchers in both the behaviour of designers and in designing for human behaviour (Design Research Society Meeting on Design Behaviour, Birmingham 1972; Design Research Society/Design Methods Group joint conference on the Design Activity, September 1972), and an increasing amount of work on presentation of information (52, 53, 54).

A further component of the integration problem is complementary to the last one. It is that designers, engineers, management etc. don't know enough about ergonomics either to use it (or ergonomists) or to estimate its value to them. If ergonomics really is of value, then this particular problem will be resolved with the passing of time, as long as ergonomists continue to work, and as long as ergonomics continues to permeate into education.

A fourth component relating to integration concerns the placing of the ergonomist in an organization wishing to employ him. Where does he fit? The multi- disciplinary nature of the subject has double-edged relevance to this question. The ergonomist can fit into a number of departments. Singleton (55) for example, describes how an ergonomist might be based in design and production engineering departments, work study departments, medical departments, operational research departments, and sometimes the personnel department. Thus there are many possible locations. On the other hand ergonomics is relevant to all these activities and location in any one of them may (because of inter-departmental conflict etc.) mean an under utilization of the ergonomist's skills.

Sometimes, then, a separate ergonomics department is required. However, this in turn can be bedevilled by interdepartmental problems. Additional, as opposed to integrated disciplines are easier to ignore. There is no one solution to this problem. It depends on the ergonomist, the organization and its approach. Much the same problem exists in education. Ergonomics is relevant to most types of engineering, to architecture, to building and to design courses. The choice exists between including ergonomics in each of these courses or in setting up a separate department (which might run service courses for the others). Neither of these solutions is particularly satisfactory for the basic reason that our universities are not organized for multi-disciplinary education. It would seem that there is a need for a reorganization of both educational and industrial practice, and there are signs that this is happening as the interest in and recognition of the value of multi-disciplinary studies grows.

Meanwhile, there remains the crucial problem concerning the demonstration of the value of ergonomics. Meister (6) suggests that in order to demonstrate both the relevance and value of ergonomics (to building, for example) it is necessary to:

1. show that human errors occur in sufficient numbers, and
2. that such errors result from deficiencies in design, production, maintenance and use, and
3. that errors have significant effects, and
4. that ergonomics can reduce error potential and improve performance.

This would be an ambitious undertaking, but it is worth doing. Meister defines error as *a deviation from some specified objective or desired performance*. This is sufficient as long as the objectives and desired performance are specified. There is however another vitally important type of error and this is *inadequate definition of objectives*. (The first type of error breaking specified rules—is sometimes called a *formal error*, the second type—inadequate problem definition—is called a *substantive error*). Ergonomics can be of value in rectifying formal errors in conventional settings, but can also be useful in indentifying substantive errors. In fact the continued existence of the subject can be seen as an attempt to correct a most important type of substantive error; namely that technology is more important than people, and, at a more specific level, that machines should, wherever possible, replace people.

There is considerable evidence that these viewpoints are both foolish and erroneous. There is also evidence of the limits to technological growth, and that machines are not capable of replacing human beings in many of the most important areas of human life. Ergonomics can contribute to stopping the technological tail wagging the dog.

REFERENCES

1. EDHOLM, O. G. 1(1967). *The Biology of Work* (World University Library).
2. FUCIGNA, J. T. (1967). 'The Ergonomics of Offices.' *Ergonomics* 10 (5), 589–604.
3. VAN WELY, P. (1970). 'Design and Disease.' *Applied Ergonomics* 1 (5).
4. BEEVIS, D. and SLADE, I. M. (1970). 'Ergonomics—Costs and Benefits'. *Applied Ergonomics* 1 (2), 79–84.
5. BOWEN, H. M. (1967). 'The imp in the system'. *Ergonomics* 10 (2), 112–119.
6. MEISTER, D. (1971). *Human Factors* (London: Wiley).
7. DAVIS, L. E. and TAYLOR, J. C. (1972). *Design of Jobs* (London: Penguin).
8. RYAN, M. (1972). *Designing with Man in Mind*. International Symposium on the Environment in Buildings. Loughborough Univ.
9. GRALL, T. B. (1972). *Environmental Design & Research for the Non-Ambulatory*. International Symposium on the Environment in Buildings, Loughborough University.
10. LANGDON, F. J. (1972). *Human Sciences and the Environment in Buildings: an Appraisal and Critique*. International Symposium on the Environment in Buildings, Loughborough University.
11. PAGE, J. K. (1960). 'Some Ergonomic Problems Confronting the Building Designer.' *Ergonomics,* 3 (2), 133–140.
12. WARD, J. S. (1970). 'Ergonomics in the Home' *Applied Ergonomics* 1 (4) 223–227.
13. WARD, J. S. and KIRK, N. S. (1970). 'The Relation between Anthropometric Dimensions and Preferred Working Surface Heights in the Kitchen.' *Ergonomics,* 13 (6), 783–793.
14. SHEPPARD, N., and MAHADDIE, C. (1970). 'Kitchen Worktop Heights.' *Architects J. Information Library* 30th Sept., 797–730.
15. WARD, J. S. and RANDALL, P. (1967). 'Optimum Dimensions for Domestic Stairways: a Preliminary Study.' *Architects' Journal*, 5th July.
16. HYDE, W. T. (1972). 'Window Operation.' *Building.* 17th Nov. 151–155.
17. YAFFE, B. (1968). 'Functional and Ergonomic Requirements of Door Furniture.' *Design Research Laboratory Report No.* 3 (16), (U.M.I.S.T.: Dept. of Building).
18. HILL, A. R. (1969). Vision through Meshes: a summary report. *Lighting Research & Technology*, 1 (1), 54–56.
19. GRIEVE, J. I. (1972). 'Heart Rate and Daily Activities of Housewives with Young Children.' *Ergonomics,* 15 (2), 139–146.
20. MENDICK, A. H. (1972). 'Designing for the Aged.' *3rd Year Project Report* (Dept. of Building, U.M.I.S.T.).
21. KENWARD, M. G. (1971). 'An approach to the Design of Wheelchairs for young users.' *Applied Ergonomics,* 2 (4), 221–225.
22. OLDFIELD, J. J. (1972). *Survey of the Housing & Equipment Provision of Registered Physically Disabled People.* (Institute of Advanced Studies, Manchester Polytechnic).
23. GOLDSMITH, S. (1972). Designing for the Disabled—The Problems of Conflicting Criteria. *International Symposium on the Environment in Buildings, Loughborough University.*
24. LEONARD, J. A. (1972). 'Studies in Blind Mobility.' *Applied Ergonomics.* 3 (1), 37–46.
25. BEST, G. A. (1967). 'Direction-Finding in Large Buildings.' *Design Research Laboratory Report No.* 3 (13), (UMIST: Dept. of Building).
26. CORLETT, E. N., MANENICA, I. and BISHOP R. P. (1972). 'The Design of Direction-Finding systems in Buildings.' *Applied Ergonomics* 3 (2), 66–69.

27. DE JONG, J. R. (1971). 'The Effectiveness of Equipment for the Users.' *Applied Ergonomics* **2** (2), 104–111.
28. POYNER, B. (1972). 'Barriers and Communication' *International Symposium on the Environment in Buildings.* Loughborough University.
29. WEBSTER, J. N. (1968). 'The Behaviour of Door Users' MSC Dissertation. *Design Research Laboratory Report No.* 3 (22), (UMIST: Dept. of Building).
30. PRATT, D. J. (1968). 'Building in bad weather: 1. On-Site problems in Winter,' *National Builder.* **49** (9), 536–539.
31. MACKWORTH, N. H. (1953). 'Finger numbness in very cold winds.' *J. Appl. Phys.* **5**, 533–543.
32. RUSSELL, R. W. (1957). 'Effects of variations in ambient temperature on certain measures of tracking skill and sensory sensitivity. *US Army MRL Project No.* 6–95–20–001 Report No. 300.
33. TEICHNER, W. H. (1956). 'Reaction time in the cold.' *J. Appl. Phys.*, **42**, 54–59.
34. PROVINS, K. A. (1958). 'Environmental Conditions and Driving Efficiency.' *Ergonomics*, **2**, 97–107.
35. POULTON, E. C. (1958). 'The Environment at Work.' *Applied Ergonomics* **3** (1), 24–29.
36. WILKINSON, R. (1970). 'Productivity and the Environment.' *Applied Ergonomics* **1** (4).
37. TEIGH, R. H. (1972). *Handling Weights without Injury.* (ICI Ltd., Millbank, London).
38. ANON (1970). *Manual Lifting* (Abstract in Occupational Safety and Health Abstracts).
39. WHITNEY, R. J. (1958). 'The Strength of the Lifting Action in Man.' *Ergonomics* **1**, 101–128.
40. BOBBERT, A. C. (1960). 'Optimal form and dimensions of hand-grips on certain concrete building blocks.' *Ergonomics* **3**, (2), 141–148.
41. GARRETT, J. W. (1971). 'The Adult Human Hand: Some Anthropometric and Biomechanical Considerations.' *Human Factors* **13** (2), 117–131.
42. DATTA, S. R. and RAMANATHAN, N. (1971). 'Ergonomic Comparison of Seven Modes of carrying loads on the horizontal plane.' *Ergonomics* **14** (2), 269–278.
43. STRINDBERG, L. and PETTERSSON, N. F. (1971). 'Measurement of Force Perception in Pushing Trolleys.' *Ergonomics.* **15** (4), 435–438.
44. ERS Industrial Committee (1971). Conference on *Human Factors in Materials Handling.* Includes papers by Troup, Wadsworth and others. Report in *Applied Ergonomics* **2** (2), p. 126–7.
45. CORLETT, E. N. and WHITE, T. G. (1968). 'Crane Drivers in Danger'. *Design,* 237, 66–69.
46. ARKELL, R. K., CAMPBELL, A. M. MARTEN, P. L., MENDICK, A. H. and WOODCOCK, N. P. (1972). *Motor Grader Evaluation.* Ergonomics Project Report, Dept. of Building, UMIST.
47. CONRAN, H. (1972). 'Good Conditions can Improve Performance.' *Construction Plant and Equipment,* November 1972, 48–50.
48. WIMPEY NEWS (1972). 'TV Eye puts a safe end to crane driver's dilemma' *Issue* **372**, p. 3.
49. SELL, R. G. (1971). 'Ergonomics Versus Accidents.' *Applied Ergonomics* **2** (1) (Chapter 12, Applied Ergonomics Handbook).
50. SINGLETON, W. T. (1972). 'Techniques for determining the Causes of Error.' *Applied Ergonomics.* **3** (3), 126–131.
51. CHAPANIS, A. (1970). 'Relevance of Physiological and Psychological Criteria to Man-Machine Systems. The Present State of the Art.' *Ergonomics*, **13** (3), 337–346.
52. WRIGHT, P. and FOX, K. (1970). 'Presenting Information in Tables.' *Applied Ergonomics,* **2** (2).
53. SPENCER, J. and MILNES-WALKER, N. D. (1971). 'The Ergonomic Study of Engineering Drawings'. *Applied Ergonomics,* **2** (3), 162–170.

54. GOODEY, J. and MATTHEW K. (1971). 'Technical information for Architects.' *Applied Ergonomics* **2** (4), 198–204.
55. SINGLETON, W. T. (1970). 'The Industrial Use of Ergonomics' *Applied Ergonomics* **1** (1).
56. MILLER, R. B. (1962). 'Task description and analysis'. *Psychological Principles in Systems Development.* Ed. Gagné, R. M., Chapter 6. (New York: Holt, Reinhart and Winston).

BIBLIOGRAPHY

A. General Ergonomics References

1. CHAPANIS, A. (1959). *Research Techniques in Human Engineering* (Baltimore: John Hopkins.)
2. DAMON, A., STOUDT, H. W. and McFARLAND, R. A. (1966). *The Human Body in Equipment Design* (Cambridge, Mass.: Harvard University Press).
3. FITTS, P. and POSNER, M. (1968). *Human Performance* (Brooks/Cole Publishing Co: Belmont).
4. FOGEL, L. J. (1963). *Biotechnology: Concepts & Applications* (Englewood Cliffs. N.J.: Prentice-Hall).
5. GAGNE, R. M. (ed.) (1962). *Psychological Principles in System Development* (New York: Holt).
6. GRANDJEAN, E. (1969). *Fitting the Task to the Man* (London: Taylor & Francis).
7. HOLDING, D. (1969) *Experimental Psychology in Industry* (Penguin).
8. McCORMICK, E. J. (1967). *Human Engineering* (New York: McGraw Hill).
9. McCULLOUGH, W. (1970). *Physical Working Conditions* (London: Gower Press).
10. MORGAN, C. T., COOK, J. S., CHAPANIS, A., and LUND, M. W. (1963). *Human Engineering Guide to Equipment Design* (New York: McGraw Hill).
11. MURREL, K. F. H. (1965). *Ergonomics* (London: Chapman & Hall).
12. SINGLETON, W. T., EASTERBY, R. S., WHITFIELD, D. (eds.) (1967). *The Human Operator in Complex Systems* (London: Taylor & Francis).
13. SINGLETON, W. T., FOX, J. G., and WHITFIELD, D. (1971). *Measurement of Man at Work* (London: Taylor & Francis).
14. WELFORD, A. T. (1968). *Fundamentals of Skill* (London: Methuen).
15. WOODSON, W. E. and CONOVER, D. W. (1964). *Human Engineering Guide for Equipment Designers* (Berkley, Calif: UCLA).

B. Building Ergonomics References

1. ANON (No date). 'Bricklaying in Cold Weather'. *Supplement to The Brick Bulletin.*
2. BATESON, R. G., NOBLE, J. K. and ATTENBURROW, J. J. (1954). 'The House and Housework.' *RIBA Journal.* Dec. 1954, 66–72.
3. BINKHORST, R. A. and CARSLOO, S. (1962). 'The Thumb-Forefinger Grip and the Shape of Handles of Certain Instruments: An Electromyographic Study of the Muscle-Load.' *Ergonomics* 5 (3), 467–470.
4. DUNCAN, C. J. (ed.) (1966). *Modern Lecture Theatres.* (London: Oriel Press).
5. FARR, M. (1967). *Ergonomics in the Design of Consumer Products.* 3rd IEA Congress on Ergonomics, Birmingham.
6. HANKIN, B. D., and WRIGHT, R. A. (1958). 'Passenger Flow in Subways' *Operational Research Quarterly* 9 (2), 81–88.
7. HANSSON, J. E. (1970). 'Ergonomics in the Building Industry.' *National Swedish Institute for Building Research.* Report No. R.8.
8. HANUSOVA, V. (1969) (a). 'Physiological basis for deterioration of rest periods in masons—first part; masoning' (in Czech) *Pracovni Lekarstvi,* 21 (6).
9. HANUSOVA, V. (1969) (b). 'Physiological basis for deterioration of rest periods in masons—second part; plastering' (in Czech) *Pracovni Lekarstvi* 21 (7). (Abstracts in *Applied Ergonomics* 3 (3) Sept. 1972 183.)
10. KINNEBURGH, W. and VALLANCE, L. S. (1948). 'A Work Study in Block Laying.' *National Building Stud. Tech. Paper No. 1.* (London: HMSO).

11. MALHOTRA, M. S. *et al.* (1966). 'Physical Work Capacity as Influenced by Age'. *Ergonomics* 9 (4). 305–316.
12. MULLER, E. A., VETTER, K. and BUMMEL, E. (1958). 'Transport by Muscle Power over Short Distances.' *Ergonomics* 1, 222–225.
13. PASSMORE, R. and DURNIN, J. W. (1955). 'Human Energy Expenditure.' *Physiol Rev.* 35, 801–839.
14. POULTON, E. C. and KERSLAKE, D.McK. (1965). 'Initial Stimulating Effect of Warmth upon Perceptual Efficiency'. *Aerospace Medicine.* 36 (1), 29–32.
15. PUGH, L. G. C. E., and CHRENKO, F. A. (1966). 'The Effective Area of the Human Body with respect to Direct Solar Radiation. *Ergonomics.* 9 (1), 63–67.
16. RAMBOUR, E. (1970). 'Safety in the use of hand-tools: hammers (in French) *Travail et Securite* No. 8. 383–389 (Abstract in Applied Ergonomics 3 (2)).
17. SPEIGHT, B. A. (1968). 'Maintenance of Buildings: Its relationship to Design.' *Building* 18th October. 117–180.
18. SWEDISH NATIONAL INSTITUTE FOR BUILDING RESEARCH (1970). 'Anatomy for Planners II–IV.' *NSBR Summaries* R12. 1970.
19. TALBOT, R. J. (1970). *Notes on Everyday Ergonomics* (Design Research Laboratory: UMIST).
20. TALBOT, R. J. (1971). 'The Integration of Ergonomics Information in Design.' *BRS Industrial Committee Conference on the Design and Evaluation of Consumer Products.* London, Sept. 1971.
21. WARD, J. S. (1971). Bibliography of work relating to domestic storage and the domestic environment. *Personal Communication.*
22. WEBSTER, C. J. D. and McTAGGERT, G. (1957). 'Packed bricks and brick handling'. *Builder* Nov. 873–6.
23. WYNDHAM, C. H. *et al.* (1966). 'The Relationship between Energy Expenditure and Performance Index in the Task of Shovelling Sand.' *Ergonomics* 9 (5), 371–378.
24. DAVIES B. T. (1972). 'Moving loads manually'. *Applied Ergonomics* 3 (3), 190–194.
25. CORLETT, E. N., HUTCHESON, C., DeLUGAN, M.A., and ROGOZENSKI, J. (1972). 'Ramps or Stairs: the choice of using physiological and biomechanic criteria'. *Applied Ergonomics* 3 (4), 195–201.
26. HOPKINSON, R. G. (1972). 'Glare from daylighting in buildings.' *Applied Ergonomics* 3 (4), 206–215.
27. RAMSAY, H. T., and SENNECK, C. R. (1972). 'Anti-slip studs for safety footwear.' *Applied Ergonomics* 3 (4), 219–223.
28. BROOKES, M. J. (1972). 'Office Landscape—does it work?' *Applied Ergonomics* 3 (4), 224–236.
29. STEIDL, R. E., and BRATTON, E. C. (1968). *Work in the Home* (New York: Wiley).

Progress in Construction Science and Technology No. 1

The first issue of Progress in Construction Science and Technology contained a unique series of research reviews. Details of the contents are given on the following pages. Copies of this volume may be obtained in the United States from

Barnes and Noble,
10 East 53rd Street,
New York,
NY 10022,
U.S.A.

and elsewhere copies should be ordered from

Medical and Technical Publishing Co. Ltd
P.O. Box 55,
St. Leonard's House,
Lancaster,
England

who will either supply the order direct or through their agents. Alternatively copies may be ordered through your local bookseller.

1
Sound insulation of partitions

H. Derrick Parbrook, BSc, PhD
Professor of Building Science,
University of Liverpool
Kenneth A. Mulholland, BSc, MSc (Eng), PhD
Lecturer in Building Science,
University of Liverpool

2

Plastics and plastics-based composites

Albert G. H. Dietz
Professor of Building Engineering,
Massachusetts Institute of Technology

2.1 Introduction

2.2. Properties
2.2.1. Strength
2.2.2. Stiffness
2.2.3. Toughness
2.2.4. Hardness
2.2.5. Optical characteristics
2.2.6. Thermal characteristics
2.2.7. Moisture permeability
2.2.8. Durability
2.2.9. Fire-resistance
2.2.10 Examples of non-structural uses of plastics in building

2.3 Composites
2.3.1. Fibrous composites
2.3.2. Examples of plastics-based composities in building
2.3.3. Laminates
2.3.4. Structural sandwiches

2.4. Auxiliaries
2.4.1. Wood
2.4.2. Masonry and concrete modifiers
2.4.3. Adhesives
2.4.4. Sealants
2.4.5. Coatings

3

Weather as a factor in building design and construction

John K. Page, BA
Professor of Building Science,
University of Sheffield

3.1. Introduction

3.2. The physical nature of problems encountered in building climatology
    3.2.1. Classification of fundamental physical problems
    3.2.2. Momentum transfer problems
    3.2.3. Mass transfer problems
    3.2.4. Energy transfer problems

3.3. Meteorological techniques for describing weather
    3.3.1. Statistical versus real-time meteorological descriptions
    3.3.2. The nature of basic meteorological information used for forecasting and climatological purposes

3.4. Concepts of macroclimate, mesoclimate, and microclimate
    3.4.1. Macroclimate
    3.4.2. Mesoclimate or local climate
    3.4.3. Microclimate
    3.4.4. Cryptoclimate
    3.4.5. Importance of vertical variations

3.5. Concept of microclimatic indices

3.6. The use of meteorological data for decision-making in the building process

3.6.1. Design against meteorological failure
3.6.2. Dynamic versus static models of failure
3.6.3. Destructive failures and extreme value analysis
3.6.4. Combinations of meteorological loadings
3.6.5. Weather and decision-making in environmental design
3.6.6. Design against weather exclusion
3.6.7. Failure of materials due to climatological causes

3.7. Operational aspects of building climatology

3.7.1. General considerations
3.7.2. Basic analysis
3.7.3. Principle factors causing loss of production
3.7.4. Low temperatures
3.7.5. Cold-weather working
3.7.6. Precipitation and the construction process
3.7.7. Rainfall types
3.7.8. Frontal rain
3.7.9. Heavy rainfall
3.7.10. Snow
3.7.11. State of ground
3.7.12. Daylight availability
3.7.13. High winds and site stoppages
3.7.14. Forecast services and building

3.8. Conclusion

Appendix. Selected sources of data on local climate, microclimate and building climatology in the United Kingdom

4

The computer as an aid to architectural design: present and future

Dr Thomas W. Maver
Director, Architecture and Building Aids Computer Unit,
University of Strathclyde, Glasgow

4.5. Future developments
4.5.1. Government policy
4.5.2. Changes in professional practice
4.5.3. Integrated systems

Appendix 4.1. Selected bibliography of decision-making programs

Appendix 4.2. Selected bibliography of management programs

5

The weathering of organic building materials

H. E. Ashton
Division of Building Research,
National Research Council of Canada, Ottawa

6
Non-destructive testing of concrete

R. H. Elvery, BSc (Eng), CEng, FICE, MI Struct E
*Senior Lecturer, Department of Civil and Municipal Engineering,
University College, London*

J. A. Forrester, BSc
*Chief Chemist, Cement and Concrete Association,
Wrexham Springs, Slough, Bucks*

7

Building in hot climates

Balwant Singh Saini, PhD, BA, BArch, FRAIA, FRIBA
Department of Architecture and Building,
University of Melbourne

7.1. Hot climates

7.2. Building design
    7.2.1. Design for human comfort
    7.2.2. Structure
    7.2.3. Glass
    7.2.4. Roofs
    7.2.5. Floors
    7.2.6. Design for extreme climatic conditions

7.3. Building materials
    7.3.1. Materials in hot humid climates
    7.3.2. Materials in hot dry climates
    7.3.3. Structural materials
    7.3.4. Paints and bituminous materials

7.4. Labour
    7.4.1. Availability
    7.4.2. Efficiency

7.5. Building techniques
    7.5.1. Construction sectors
    7.5.2. Industrialized building

7.6. Housing
    7.6.1. The housing shortage
    7.6.2. Self-help schemes

8
Principles of structural fire-resistance

H. L. Malhotra, BSc (Eng), CEng, MICE,
Head of the Structural and Materials Fire Test Section,
Fire Research Station, Boreham Wood

8.1. Introduction

8.2. Brief history of statutory control

8.3. Pattern of a fire

8.4. Aim of structural fire protection

8.5. Fire-resistance and its determination
    8.5.1. General
    8.5.2. Stability
    8.5.3. Specimen size
    8.5.4. Apparatus

8.6. Properties of materials at high temperatures
    8.6.1. General
    8.6.2. Steel
    8.6.3. Aluminium
    8.6.4. Concrete
    8.6.5. Wood
    8.6.6. Plastics

8.7. Behaviour of structures in a fire

8.8. Design features of structural elements
    8.8.1. Beams
    8.8.2. Floors
    8.8.3. Walls
    8.8.4. Columns

8.9. Future trends in fire protection

9

Structural lightweight aggregate concrete

Adrian Pauw
Professor of Engineering,
University of Missouri